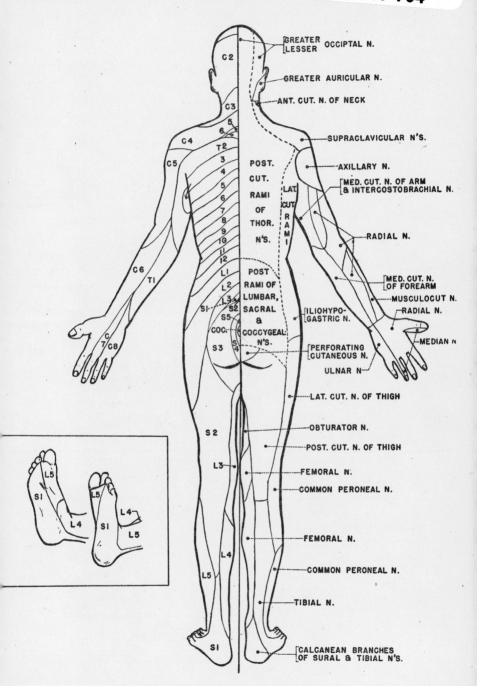

PAIN

Publication Number 333

AMERICAN LECTURE SERIES®

A *Monograph in*

The BANNERSTONE DIVISION *of*

AMERICAN LECTURES IN PHYSIOLOGY

Edited by

ROBERT F. PITTS, M.D., PH.D.
Professor of Physiology and Biophysics
Cornell University Medical College
New York, New York

Second Edition

PAIN

By

HAROLD G. WOLFF, M.D.

Professor of Medicine (Neurology)
Cornell University Medical College
New York City

And

STEWART WOLF, M.D.

Professor and Head, Department of
Medicine
University of Oklahoma School of
Medicine
Oklahoma City, Oklahoma

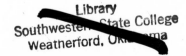
CHARLES C THOMAS · PUBLISHER
Springfield · Illinois · U.S.A.

CHARLES C THOMAS · PUBLISHER
BANNERSTONE HOUSE
301-327 East Lawrence Avenue, Springfield, Illinois, U.S.A.

Published simultaneously in the British Commonwealth of Nations by
BLACKWELL SCIENTIFIC PUBLICATIONS, LTD., OXFORD, ENGLAND

Published simultaneously in Canada by
THE RYERSON PRESS, TORONTO

First Edition, First Printing, January, 1948
First Edition, Second Printing, December, 1949
First Edition, Third Printing, December, 1951
Second Edition, First Printing, October, 1958

Library of Congress Catalog Card Number: 58-8438

With THOMAS BOOKS careful attention is given to all details of
manufacturing and design. It is the Publisher's desire to present books
that are satisfactory as to their physical qualities and artistic possibilities
and appropriate for their particular use. THOMAS BOOKS will be true
to those laws of quality that assure a good name and good will.

Printed in the United States of America

PREFACE

In this second edition the authors have attempted not
only to bring the data up-to-date but to add a few items
of practical value which had been left out of the earlier
edition. Since the publication of the most recent printing
of the first edition, there have appeared four monographs
in English, one with special reference to historical aspects,[1] one to physiology,[2] another to the use of local anesthesia,[3] and the fourth to the neurosurgical management
of pain.[4] The reader is referred to these for a detailed
account of the historical background of research on Pain
with an analysis of the significant contributions over the
years. The present volume offers a brief synthesis of the
current thinking on pain in the perspective of some of
the important past developments. It is also intended to
be a serviceable handbook for students and practitioners
who must concern themselves with day-to-day problems
in the diagnosis and management of painful conditions.
The original studies which are recapitulated and reviewed
here have been the work of numerous investigators col-
laborating with the senior author. Notable among these
workers are James D. Hardy, Helen Goodell and Bronson
S. Ray. The contributions of these and other colleagues is
gratefully acknowledged. We also wish to thank Dr. Robert F. Pitts and Charles C Thomas, Publisher, for their
patience and indulgence and Ruth Pinsky Redmont for
valuable editorial assistance.

H. G.W.

S.W.

66133

TABLE OF CONTENTS

[vii]

LIST OF ILLUSTRATIONS

[ix]

PAIN

Chapter I

ANATOMY AND PHYSIOLOGY

THE NATURE OF PAIN

Pain is one of Man's major concerns. Probably more than any other symptom pain is responsible for bringing the patient to the doctor. Thus to the clinician the understanding of pain becomes a paramount concern. Despite the importance of pain in diagnosis and the challenge it offers in therapy, however, the doctor has no certain way of knowing how much pain his patient is experiencing. As in the case of other sensations, he knows of the pain only through the patient's testimony. Unlike other sensations, however, such as smell, sight, and hearing, or even touch, temperature, pressure and vibration the particular experience cannot be shared by the examiner. Only the patient can feel his pain. The difficulty of appraising the situation makes the study of pain all the more fascinating. If a patient feels a gurgling in his abdomen, the doctor can often hear it through his stethoscope. Similarly if he feels an irregularity in his heart beat, the doctor has a dependable way of checking it, but there is no sure way to confirm the presence of pain.

With sensations other than pain the doctor is concerned with the patient's capacity to experience them and not so much with what he is actually experiencing. With pain, although capacity may be impaired, the source and significance of the pain are more often the relevant considerations for the physician.

[3]

Man since his earliest days has been concerned with methods of avoiding or dealing with pain. Pain has become recognized as an important warning of danger to the organism although it is not essential to a suitable biological adjustment. Persons congenitally without the ability to experience pain adequately adjust themselves to their environment,[5, 6] as do persons who have had pain pathways surgically interrupted. West studied a child with congenital absence of pain sensation. He found that, although she had sustained extensive joint damage as a consequence of a painless fracture which had been inadequately immobilized, she cried as a normal child would in response to the humiliation of a spanking.[7]

Alarm or defense reactions may be initiated by any stimulus if that stimulus has been previously associated with injuries, dangerous threat situations or frustrations.[8] As a matter of fact, the bulk of such reactions involved in common experience are initiated by nonpainful stimuli. Moreover, persons critically ill, as with terminal neoplastic disease, and those gravely injured do not inevitably experience intense pain. Indeed, the intensity of pain is not directly proportional to the extent or severity of tissue damage. Beecher in a combat zone during World War II questioned 215 recently wounded men concerning the intensity of the pain they were experiencing. These men had sustained extensive soft tissue injuries, compound fractures or penetrating wounds of the head, chest or abdomen, but were mentally clear. Only 24 per cent had "bad pain" whereas the remainder had moderate, slight or no pain.[9]

The management of pain constitutes a serious clinical problem, not only because of itself, as a distressing experience, but also because continued pain has been demonstrated to have deleterious action upon such vital organs as the heart [10] and kidneys.[11] Indeed pain has been shown characteristically to set off a variety of reaction patterns within the body which have been interpreted as protective and which may include occlusion of nasal passages with or without lacrimation,[12] cardiospasm,[13] disturbances of gastric and colonic functions,[14] cardiac arrhythmias [15] and elevation of arterial pressure.[16] When such bodily changes are sustained they may themselves lead to significant impairment of function or perhaps to actual tissue damage. Thus, it seems likely that pain itself may irritate or perpetuate a biologically destructive vicious cycle.

Only within the past one hundred years have medical investigators become fully aware that pain is a specific sensory experience separate and distinct from all other sensations and mediated through its own neural equipment. It is true that a stimulus which incites other sensations such as pressure, heat and cold may also induce pain but it does so by exciting the mechanism for pain as well as that for the other sensation in question. In the case of thermal stimuli, for example, this has been demonstrated by partially blocking a peripheral nerve with procaine so that pain sensation was abolished while cold was still felt.[17] It was possible to produce this effect because "cold pain" is carried in the slenderer fibers of Gasser's class C.[18] These become infiltrated with procaine before the thicker fibers which subserve the sensation of cold itself. Conversely, when partial block was induced by ischemia, cold sensation was obliterated before pain.[19] Ischemia affects the relatively thick, hard to nourish fibers which carry cold sensation before it does the slender fibers which transmit "cold pain." [20]

PATHWAYS FOR PAIN

Impulses for pain originate in naked nerve terminals scattered throughout the skin, subcutaneous structures and viscera.[21, 22, 23, 24] From these endings impulses are carried through myelinated and non-myelinated fibers of various sizes to the posterior root ganglia or the corresponding sensory ganglia in the head. Since the studies of Woollard *et al.*,[22] who stained the nerve terminals in an area of skin that was only capable of feeling pain, it has been generally accepted that the terminals are specific for the sensation, pain. More recent evidence, however, indicates that nerves connected with these endings may carry impulses for touch as well as pain.[4] Fibers may travel directly to the posterior root ganglia in somatic nerves or indirectly in sympathetic trunks [25, 26, 27, 28, 29] and through sympathetic ganglia to the posterior root ganglia via the white rami communicantes.[30]

Sensory nerve fibers have been classified according to the speed with which they conduct impulses as well as according to their size. Erlanger and Gasser measured the speed of transmission of afferent impulses by oscillographic recording of action potentials.[20, 31] They found that the small fibers were slow conducting and the large fibers conducted more rapidly. The large myelinated fibers ranging up to 20μ in diameter conduct at speeds up to 100 meters a second. They have been designated as belonging to class A. Class B fibers are also myelinated but smaller, being less than 3μ in diameter. They conduct impulses at a rate of from 3 to 14 meters per second. Class C comprises unmyelinated fibers which conduct at less than 2 meters per second. The demonstration of the existence of a fast and slow pain is easily made with the application of a single appropriate stimulus. Gasser suggests flipping the back of the finger near the nail bed against a hot electric light bulb.[25] "There are felt two distinct flashes of pain, the one coming almost at once, the other after a discernible delay . . . the second may be more intense and prolonged. A similar double flash can be felt after a needle prick." Gordon and Whitteridge have been able to correlate the reception of impulses from fast and slow pain with changes of the alpha rhythm in the electro-encephalograph.[32]

Bright, pricking pain appears to be felt in the thick, rapidly conducting myelinated fibers. Burning pain felt in the skin is transported like "cold pain" by fibers of small size which conduct more slowly. Aching pains in the muscles, bones and viscera result from impulses carried mainly in afferent fibers that proceed toward the dorsal root ganglion via sympathetic chains presumably in both myelinated and non-myelinated fibers of varying size.[33, 34] Burning pain can be induced, as shown by Forster, by stimulation of the cut peripheral end of a sensory nerve if the innervation of adjacent areas is intact.[35] The mechanism of the phenomenon may depend upon the liberation of some substance at the terminals of the cut nerve which, in turn, stimulates terminals of adjacent nerves.

The cell bodies of all sensory nerves are found in the posterior root ganglia. From there dendrites of neurons which subserve pain enter the cord along the posterior horn. Here the impulses switch to a second neuron whose cell body is in the posterior horn and are promptly transferred either directly or through additional internuncial neurons to the opposite side of the cord via the anterior commissure. Without any further synapses the impulses ascend to the lateral nucleus of the thalamus in the lateral spinothalamic tract.[36, 37] There is evidence however that some fibers ascend to the ipsilateral side and do not cross at all [38, 39] and that some phylogenetically older fibers travel in the spinotectal tracts to end in the roof nuclei of the mesencephalon.[40] Those impulses which travel to the thalamus give off branches to the reticular formation along the way. Impulses traveling into the reticular formation are thought to contribute to the mechanisms responsible for consciousness and may be important in supplying electrical energy for a variety of brain circuits. In the thalamus, fibers are transferred to additional neurons which are located in the thalamo-cortical radiation. Connections are made with the limbic system as well as with the postcentral area of the cerebral cortex, where the arrangement is such that those fibers from the medial portion of the thalamic nucleus (cephalad parts of the body) end in the lower part of the postcentral gyrus. Those from the lateral portion of the thalamic nucleus (caudad parts of the body) end in the paracentral region and those from the middle in the intermediate region. From here, connections are made to the highest integrative levels [41] within the cerebral hemispheres for the interpretation of the painful sensation and doubtless the formulation of the individual's reaction toward it.

The ramifying cortical connections lead to the interpretation of most painful experiences as disagreeable but it must be remembered that these supratentorial connections are very numerous and would appear to differ from person to person. Many of the connections which give pain experiences their meaning peculiar to the individual may be in the nature of relays and circuits which have been laid down in the cerebral cortex in the course of past experiences. Because of these multifarious associations for pain in the interpretive areas of the cortex, pain is no more a simple perception of a sensory experience than insult is a simple perception of a sound. Figure 1 shows a diagrammatic representation of pathways for pain.

THE STIMULUS FOR PAIN

Since pain is a specific sensory experience mediated through its own nerve structures, it is evident that an adequate stimulus is required at the end organ. Although

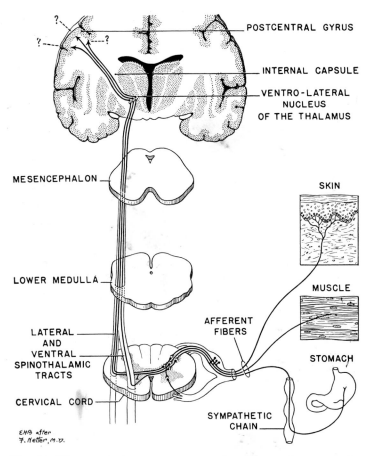

Fig. 1. Diagrammatic representation of pathways for pain. The question marks represent as yet undefined but doubtless vast numbers of connections for impulses from a single pain fiber at the highest integrative level. (Drawn by E. H. Broedel, adapted with permission from the Ciba Collection of Medical Illustrations by F. Netter, M.D.)

a great variety of noxious experiences are capable of evoking pain, the exact nature of the adequate stimulus at the nerve terminal has not been established. Hardy, Wolff and Goodell,[42] and Ostfeld, Chapman, Goodell and Wolff[43] have adduced evidence from experience with thermal radiation to the skin that tissue damage may be the common denominator. They found that the heat required to induce barely perceptible (threshold) pain was just equivalent to that required to begin alteration of tissue proteins. Moreover from painful areas Wolff *et al.*[43] have been able to recover what appears to be protein breakdown products. The thesis of Hardy, Wolff and Goodell has been rejected by Beecher on the grounds that after war wounds or surgical procedures extensive laceration and contusion and tissue injury may be unaccompanied by significant amounts of pain.[44] The contradiction is probably due to the different meaning of "tissue damage" to the two groups. The adequate stimulus for pain must be sought in the immediate vicinity of the nerve terminal. In large lacerations and contusions the nerve terminals may be protected from noxious stimulation by edema, a protective layer of fluid, inert tissue, or coagulated serum. Also the neural structures may be so damaged as to be incapable of conducting impulses. Thus the size of a laceration may not reflect the extent of tissue damage in the neighborhood of intact nerve terminals and capable of stimulating them. An additional factor which may regulate the amount of pain to follow tissue injury may be the rate at which the tissue damage occurs.

When pain endings are intact and suitably accessible, appropriate noxious stimuli applied to any bodily structure equipped with pain endings may give rise to the sensation of pain.[45, 46] Whether or not pain occurs depends upon the integrity of the pathways, the nature of the stimulus, its intensity and the individual's pain threshold.

In the case of pain from sites of inflammation there is accumulating evidence that a pain producing chemical substance may be elaborated near the nerve endings.[47] This has been partly characterized as a polypeptide with ability to produce contraction of the isolated rat uterus. It shares some of the properties of, but is not identical with 5-hydroxytryptamine.

MEASUREMENT OF THRESHOLD FOR PAIN PERCEPTION

Pain is most profitably investigated in conscious man and its occurrence is best established by verbal reports of trained subjects. Such verbal reports have been successfully used in researches on other sensations and they have yielded reproducible data in the investigation of pain. Muscle twitching, blinking and withdrawal and other responses are unreliable indicators of perception since they constitute reaction to pain and depend in part on the temperament and experience of the individual as will be discussed later.

To understand the phenomenology of pain it is appropriate first to examine data relating to pain threshold. The pain threshold sensation may be defined as the lowest perceptible intensity of pain. The pain threshold stimulus is the amount of energy required to induce threshold pain and may for convenience be expressed in standard physical terms. In accordance with common usage the pain threshold is considered to be raised when more stimulus energy is required to induce threshold pain; conversely when less stimulus energy is required, the pain threshold is said to be lowered.

Pain is unique in that many methods of stimulation can evoke it. Both superficial and deep pain can be elicited by thermal, electrical, mechanical and chemical stimuli. It is only necessary to choose a stimulus, the strength of which can be controlled and measured which will allow a clearly defined end point of perception and one which will not of itself introduce excessive variability into the observation. Establishment of the pain threshold is made by obtaining a verbal report from the stimulated subject.

Goetzl, Burrill and Ivy [48] reviewed all of the methods employed for the investigation of pain threshold up to 1942 and devised an additional one in which nerves in the teeth are stimulated with an electric current.

Chapman and Jones [49] measured the pressure required to induce pain in the esophagus by distention, and Harrison and Bigelow,[50] also studying deep pain, measured the point at which pain occurred in working ischaemic muscles of the forearm.

The shortcomings of most methods lie in the failure to establish a known relationship between the quantity measured as the stimulus and the amount of pain producing disturbance at the nerve ending. In spite of the disadvantages of these methods they have contributed much to the general body of knowledge concerning the pain experience and must be taken into account in a consideration of the nature of pain. Quantitative measurement of pain threshold requires an instrument which can induce pain without undue tissue damage by a stimulus whose intensity can be accurately measured in physical units and which can be brought to bear in predictable fashion on the structure to be stimulated.

Perhaps the most effective method of measuring cutaneous pain threshold involves the exposure of an area of skin to radiant heat (Figure 2). This method has been shown to answer the requirement stated above for the measurement of pain producing stimuli since sensory impulses arising at the end organ in the skin have been shown to be proportional to the thermal gradient and the latter to be proportional to a stimulus of radiant heat.[51, 52] Therefore, the intensity of radiation is proportional to the amount of pain producing disturbance at the end organ. By this method both pricking and burning pain threshold can be ascertained and the stimulus expressed in milligram calories per second per square centimeter. For most experimental purposes the pricking pain end point is more convenient. Hardy *et al.* have shown, however, that aching pain as measured by pressure of a dull object on the forehead behaves in most respects like pricking pain including the uniformity of threshold and effect of analgesics.[53]

The available evidence from studies with various devices indicates that all persons whose bodily structures are healthy have approximately the same capacity for perceiving pain (Figure 3). Under normal conditions this threshold does not vary from day to day or from hour to hour throughout the day (Figure 4). That is, the weakest standard stimulus required to produce a recognizable sensation of pain in one individual will have, roughly, the same intensity in all other healthy individuals. This means that the threshold for the perception of pain under normal circumstances is approximately the same in all subjects and in the same subject at varying times of the day or year.[54] There does appear to be some variability of threshold from place to place on the body. For pricking pain induced by thermal radiation Hardy *et al.* found the least sensitivity on the heel and the greatest in the region of the buttocks.[55] Hukovic and Stern correlated pain sensitivity in various parts of the body with the concentration of histamine in the skin.[56]

Pain threshold may be raised not only by analgesics [57, 58] but also by placebos [59] and autosuggestion and other maneuvers which alter the attitude of the subject. These include distractions such as induced by the clanging of a

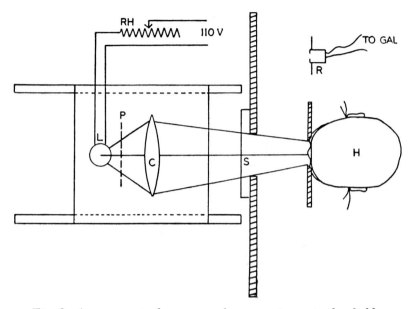

Fig. 2. Arrangement of apparatus for measuring pain thresholds.

The light from a 1000 watt lamp, *L*, was focused by a condensing lens, *C*, through a fixed aperture onto the blackened forehead of the subject, *H*. The surface of the forehead to be tested was thoroughly blackened with India ink. This measure was taken to insure total absorption of the radiation, regardless of pigmentation of the skin, and to eliminate possible effects due to the penetration of the rays below the skin surface. The stimulus could thus be considered as purely thermal.

The intensity of the radiation was controlled by means of a rheostat, *RH*. Immediately in front of the lamp was mounted an automatic shutter, *P*, which was arranged to allow the radiation to pass through to the subject for exactly three seconds. This time interval was so short that the heating of the skin was local and effects due to conduction at the edges of the aperture could be neglected. Thus, the temperature changes in the exposed area were assured to be uniform. It was necessary that the time of stimulation be fixed precisely as the pain threshold depended upon this factor. In the present apparatus *P* was fixed to a heavy pendulum. The shutter, *S*, was operated manually, and allowed stimulation of the subjects when desired.

The method of making the measurement of pain threshold was as follows: The subject seated himself and placed his forehead in position. The aperture was arranged so that 3.5 cm.^{2} of blackened skin

$\rightarrow$

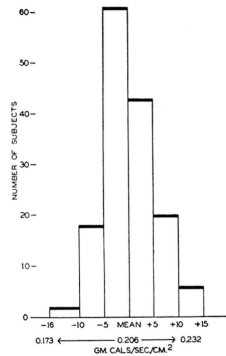

Fig. 3. Uniformity of pain threshold in 150 subjects. All of the subjects fall within ± 15 per cent of the mean.

could be exposed. After a minute or so the shutter, S, was lowered and the radiation allowed to fall on the skin for three seconds. The subject reported on his sensation. If no pain was experienced, the intensity of the light was increased and after thirty to sixty seconds the test was repeated. This procedure was followed until the subject just felt pain at the end of the exposure. This threshold pain was easily recognizable even by untrained subjects. The sensation was that of heat finally "swelling" to a distinct, sharp stab of pain at the end. When this condition had been reached the radiometer, R, was placed in the aperture in place of the forehead of the subject and the intensity of the radiation measured in gm. cal./sec./cm.^{2} This value was considered to be the minimum stimulus for pain and was shown to be proportional to any thermal changes taking place in the skin, whether the total change or rate of change of skin temperature or both be considered. The radiometer was calibrated by means of a radiation standard of the U. S. Bureau of Standards and also with an experimental black body.

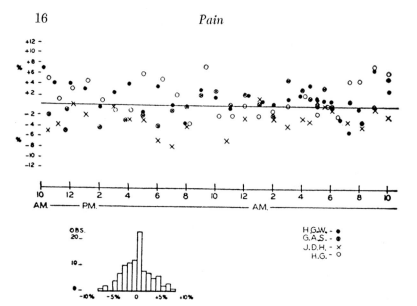

Fig. 4. Uniformity of pain threshold in four subjects from hour to hour during a twenty-four hour period.

loud bell. During hypnosis the threshold for perception of pain was raised 40 per cent. It was also possible by hypnosis to suggest pain perception at intensities of stimulation lower than threshold and actually to increase greatly the degree of tissue damage resulting from a noxious stimulus of relatively low intensity.

PRIMARY HYPERALGESIA

The term hyperalgesia describes a state in which originally non-noxious stimuli become capable of inducing pain or in which noxious stimuli induce pain of greater intensity than they normally do. One may distinguish two broad types of hyperalgesia: 1) Hyperalgesia due to a lowering of the pain threshold; 2) Hyperalgesia due to other mechanisms and occurring in the presence of normal pain threshold. The former has been called primary

because it occurs in damaged tissue and the latter secondary because, although it may be associated with injury,
the hyperalgesia itself occurs in undamaged tissue.[60] This
latter type will be discussed later under "Analysis of Deep
Pain."

Among primary hyperalgesias may be cited, for example, that occurring in peripheral neuropathy. There, hyperalgesia results from a differential effect upon the
thresholds of the two types of cutaneous pain. The
threshold for the slowly conducted cutaneous burning
pain may be greatly lowered when thresholds for the more
rapidly conducted pricking pain are elevated to the point
where the latter sensation is partially or completly abolished.[33] This effect also apparently obtains in most types
of neuritis and following injury to nerves. In Figure 5 is
contrasted the normal relationship for the threshold for
pricking and burning pain with those during hyperalgesia
after injury to nerves. The same lowering of threshold for
burning pain with simultaneous raising of that for pricking pain has been shown to occur with progressive asphyxia of nerves induced by interruption of circulation to
an extremity prior to the development of complete anesthesia. Thus have the sensory changes in peripheral neuritis due to deficiencies and "intoxication" been simulated
and analyzed.

Other local tissue changes as, for example, sustained
hyperemia and inflammation, which lower the effective
strength of stimulus required to induce pain, may also
result in hyperalgesia of the first type. It is common experience that minor, ordinarily non-noxious stimuli applied to inflamed areas on the body frequently are painful.
In the erythematous skin following exposure to ultra-
violet light, a lowering of pain threshold as much as 50
per cent was found.[61] In the mucus membranes of the
nose a similar lowering of pain threshold was found with

sustained hyperemia and inflammation [62] as well as in the mucosa of the viscera, the esophagus,[63] stomach,[64] colon [65] and bladder.[66] In fact, erroneous beliefs that these visceral mucus membranes were pain insensitive arose because noxious stimuli painful in the skin failed to elicit pain when they were applied to the viscera.[34] It is now clear that pinching, pricking or stimulation with faradic current of the mucus membrane of the turgid, hyperemic stomach, colon, or bladder, gives rise to pain. Hyperemia may have special importance with regard to the pain of peptic ulcer since the stomach in this condition is known to be overactive and its wall engorged with blood. When the stomach is in such a state, normal forceful contractions were found to be painful.[14]

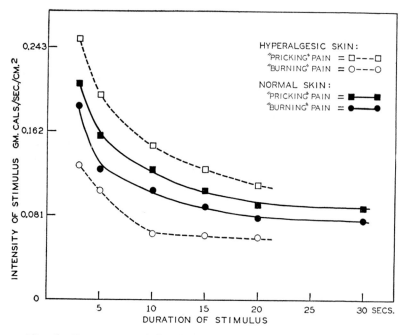

Fig. 5. Comparison of thresholds of "burning" pain to "pricking" pain in a patient with hyperalgesia as a result of radiculitis.

It appears likely, in view of the pain which commonly accompanies bronchitis, that the mucosal lining of the bronchial tree, ordinarily insensitive to pinching and pricking, becomes pain-sensitive to minor stimuli by virtue of the threshold-lowering effects of inflammation.

An important part of the mechanism responsible for hyperalgesia depends upon the local elaboration of a chemical substance which lowers pain threshold. Some of the properties of this material have been described by Ostfeld *et al.,*[43, 67, 68] in tissue fluid removed from the scalp during vascular headache of the migraine type. They found it to be similar to the pain-producing substance extracted by Armstrong *et al.* from blister fluid and inflammatory exudates.[47] It appears to be a protein breakdown product containing one or more polypeptides. The elaboration of this pain threshold lowering substance or substances in vascular headache appears to depend upon the integrity of the peripheral nerves in the area.

MEASUREMENT OF THRESHOLD FOR REACTION TO PAIN

Most pains are interpreted by the organism as unpleasant and consequently give rise to some reaction of aversion on the part of the affected subject. What he "feels," thinks, or does about it constitutes his reaction to pain. The threshold for reaction to pain, unlike the threshold for perception, varies between wide limits for given individuals and for the same individual under differing circumstances. The threshold for one type of reaction to pain was measured by an electrical device which recorded changes in skin resistance.[69] The forearm and the middle finger were connected through electrodes in contact with the skin to a Wheatstone bridge. The resistance between these points was measured and the galvanometer properly balanced. Thermal radiation was then applied for exactly three seconds to a 15 cm. area of blackened forehead of the subject, and the intensity of the radiation increased until the galvanometer needle swung sharply across the scale, following the stimulus. The amount of radiation just able to evoke this response to a heat stimulus on the forehead was called the threshold for reaction. For comparison, and using the large area of 15 cm. the threshold for pain perception was also determined in the manner already described. Figure 6 illustrates the variability of reaction thresholds in three subjects contrasted to the relative constancy of thresholds for perception of pain.

The threshold for reaction has been measured by other methods. Chapman and colleagues,[70] using radiant heat as a painful stimulus, considered a wincing response characterized by narrowing of the eyelids as an evidence of reaction to pain. They found that neurotic patients in general displayed a lower threshold for reaction than normal individuals.

Other investigators, notably Libman [71] and later Hollander,[72] whose investigations were directed toward estimation of the threshold for pain perception, actually tested reactivity. Libman exerted pressure with his thumb upon the styloid processes of human subjects and found that prize fighters, Negroes and American Indians, as groups, failed to react to some noxious stimuli of intensity great enough to induce a reaction of discomfort in the average white city dweller.

Hollander's instrument was a rough metal grater incorporated in a sphygmomanometer cuff. He inflated the cuff and noted the pressure at which the subject winced. He also learned that relatively stoical people have a high threshold for reaction to pain. Drugs such as alcohol and morphine which induce in the subject a feeling of freedom from anxiety may raise enormously the threshold for reaction to pain in addition to their influence on pain perception. The effect on pain reaction may exceed by several times the effect of an agent on pain perception.

FACTORS INVOLVED IN REACTION TO PAIN

Included in the category of reaction to pain are not only disagreeable feelings, vocal and facial expressions of displeasure and alterations in sweating in the skin but also, for example, the elevation of blood pressure which Hines and Brown [73] utilized in their "cold pressor test." Tachycardia and tapping of the feet are other reactions. They appear to imply on the part of the affected organ-

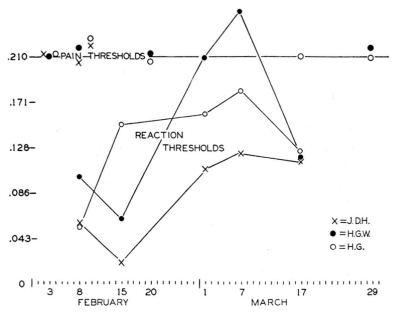

Fig. 6. A comparison of the thresholds for perception of pain with those for reaction to pain in three subjects under resting conditions.

(The ordinate = the intensity of stimulus, i.e., the amount of heat in gram calories per second per square centimeter. The abscissa = the date of the observation. Note the variability of the reaction threshold as compared with the stability of the pain threshold.)

ism a desire to run away. More serious cardiac disturbances occurring in reaction to pain have been detected as alterations in the electrical activity of the heart.[10] Other visceral disturbances such as curtailment of renal blood flow have been noted in reaction to painful experiences.[11]

DISTINCTION BETWEEN PAIN PERCEPTION AND REACTION TO PAIN

The ability to perceive pain depends upon the intactness of relatively simple and primitive nerve connections. Reaction to pain, on the other hand, is modified by the highest cognitive functions and depends in part upon what the sensation *means* to the individual in the light of his past life experience. This simple distinction between perception of pain and reaction to the experience was not at once appreciated by investigators and consequently until recently confusion existed regarding the nature of pain.[74] Man was slow to examine and define pain. Two thousand four hundred years ago when Aristotle propounded the doctrine of five senses, he included vision, hearing, taste, smell and touch but not pain. He considered pain to be a "passion of the soul." [75] Two thousand years after Aristotle's day, Erasmus Darwin, father of Charles Darwin, suggested that pain represented the exaggeration of any cutaneous sensation and pointed out that intense stimulation of the skin with heat, cold or pressure resulted in pain.[76] Sixty-five years later, in 1858, Schiff, from experiments on dogs, concluded that pain and touch must be entirely separate phenomena since noxious and tactile impulses were carried in different parts of the spinal cord.[77] This finding gave impetus to the idea that pain might be a separate sensation and was shortly followed by the critical experiments of Blix [78] and Goldscheider [79] who, working independently, demonstrated that the human skin contained specific minute spots where stimulation, by whatever method, yielded only that sensation which was characteristic for the spot, either cold, warmth, pressure or pain. This work was expanded by Von Frey, who, by the use of stiff stimulating hairs applied to the skin, was able to add further evidence of the specificity of pain as a sensation.[80] Weddell and his colleagues were able to stain characteristic naked nerve terminals for pain.[22, 23, 24]

As noted, however, the sensation pain is often associated with a reaction of anguish or displeasure and, indeed, these strong feeling states may predominate in the pain experience, becoming to the one who suffers the most relevant aspect of pain. Therefore, it becomes clear that while there is a distinction between sensory perception and the "quale," or feeling state, both formulate fundamental aspects of the pain experience.

CHARACTERISTICS OF PAIN AS A SENSATION

As already pointed out, except for a few individuals who appear to be congenitally insensitive to pain, the capacity of everyone for perception is approximately equal. Individual capacity for reaction to pain, however, is as variable from person to person as life experience itself, and it is also variable from time to time in the same individual. The quality of a painful experience is not usually very well described by patients. The pioneer experiments of Sir Thomas Lewis have led to the present recognition of several distinguishably different qualities of pain experience, namely, a bright pricking pain, a burning pain and a deeper feeling, aching pain.[34] The duration of a painful sensation, its variability and intensity, and its rhythmicity may serve further to distinguish types of pain experience based on these basic sensory patterns as they arise from various sites and in association with various disturbances. In general, cutaneous pain differs from visceral pain in possessing a bright quality which seems to exert an exhilarating action and commonly incites the individual affected to fight or flight. This pattern has biologic usefulness since assaults from a hostile environment are likely first to strike the skin. Visceral pain, on the other hand, is characterized by a deeper, aching quality which seems to exert a depressing effect, is commonly associated with nausea and followed by inactivity. This pattern, too, appears to have biologic significance since fight or flight would be fruitless against assaults from within. One cannot, for example, run away from an acutely inflamed appendix.

Not only are there distinguishable qualities of pain but there are recognizable differences in intensity. It was found possible to recall with reasonable accuracy the intensity of a given pain.[81] In the case of radiant heat focused on a spot in the blackened skin, nearly maximal pain was induced by a strength of stimulus twice that of the threshold value. At this level tissue destruction occurred. Further large increase in the strength of stimulation failed to enhance by more than one, or possibly two additional steps the intensity of pain felt. It has been shown that human subjects can discriminate approximately twenty-two increments of intensity between threshold pain and pain of maximal intensity.[81] Two such steps have been arbitrarily designated as a unit of pain, or one "dol."

The nerves which subserve pain continue to conduct the sensation as long as the stimulus is applied.[17] Thus, for painful stimuli, no true adaptation occurs as it does for touch. There may be apparent adaptation, however, when, during prolonged stimulation, the local situation in the painful part is altered so that the mechanism for pain is interrupted. For example, a pin thrust into the skin may damage a nerve terminal after originally stimulating it and thus vitiate its ability to relay impulses. Noxious stimuli may also give rise to the development of a local edema or callous formation, thus increasing the distance between stimulus and receptor.

Pain differs from other commonly experienced sensations such as sight, hearing, smell, touch and vibration in that its perception may be modified by analgesic agents. Morphine, codeine and alcohol do not affect the threshold of sensory experience other than pain as shown in Figures 6A and B.[82]

Pain has other individual qualities. From heat and cold sensations it differs in the fact that it does not display all of the phenomena of spatial summation to any substantial extent, although Hardy *et al.* has shown that a slight summative effect occurs when the size of an area subjected to noxious stimulation is greatly increased.[17, 51, 83] In general, however, when the size of the area exposed is increased, the intensity of stimulus required to produce pain shows virtually no change. Furthermore, the intensity of two pains existing separately at the same time is no greater than that of the more intense of the two. In fact, the existence of one pain actually raises the threshold for perception of another.[17] This effect was early noted by Hippocrates[84] and is made use of when persons in pain bite their lips or drive their fingernails into their palms. Gammon and Starr[85] have shown that the intensity of deep pains may be reduced by non-noxious tactile pressure and thermal stimuli applied to the skin. This effect doubtless explains the efficacy of hot water bottles and ice bags in various painful conditions. They further found that the intensity of the stimulus, to be effective in modifying deep pain, had to be just below that intensity which produced manifest discomfort when applied to normal skin. Not only was the intensity of pain modified immediately after the application of the counter irritant

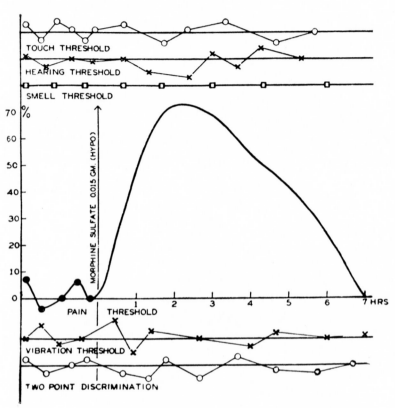

Fig. 6A. The effect of morphine sulfate on the thresholds for touch (von Frey hairs); hearing (audiometer); smell (Elsberg apparatus; vibration (Roth neurometer); and on two-point discrimination—compared with its effect on the pain threshold.

but again immediately after it had been withdrawn. These effects appear to be related to the general phenomenon of extinction; that is the elevation of perception threshold for one sensory stimulus while another is being applied. The phenomenon is especially evident among those who have sustained damage to the cerebral hemispheres.[86] Extinction of pain was demonstrated in subjects with damage to the parietal portion of one cerebral hemisphere. These subjects perceived pain from pin prick on both sides of the body, but when both sides of the body were pricked simultaneously and with equal intensity, the subjects failed to perceive pain on the side opposite the lesion. In the absence of stimulation, pain threshold was

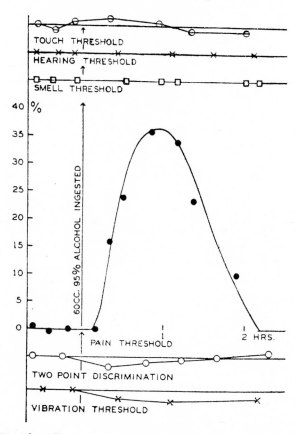

Fig. 6B. The effect of ethyl alcohol (60 cc., 95 per cent) on the thresholds for touch (von Frey hairs); hearing (audiometer); smell (Elsberg apparatus); vibration (Roth neurometer); and on two-point discrimination—compared with its effect on the pain threshold.

found to be elevated on the involved side and the threshold could be raised even further by applying noxious stimuli of increasing intensity to the intact side. Also the normal pain threshold on the intact side could be raised when intensive noxious stimuli were applied to the affected side. These phenomena can be viewed as a widespread impairment of sensory perception at a high level of integration in which the most immediate effective stimulus inhibits awareness of other noxious stimuli.

Further consideration of the nature of pain requires an analysis of the differences between cutaneous and deep pain. The latter is characterized by special associated phenomena attributable to the spread of excitation which occurs when noxious impulses subserving deep pain sensations reach the central nervous system. These associated phenomena include skeletal muscle contractions, smooth muscle and gland effects, deep and superficial hyperalgesia and hyperesthesia and reference of pain to deep and superficial structures in areas more or less remote from the site of stimulation.

ANALYSIS OF DEEP PAIN

As already mentioned, two types of cutaneous pain have been recognized, a rapidly conducted pricking sensation, bright and sharply localized and a slowly conducted burning sensation, less sharply, but still fairly well localized. Deep pains have a dull aching quality and are generally poorly localized. Noxious stimulation of widely separated nasal and paranasal structures, for example, induces pain felt initially as a burning pain at the site of stimulation which is shortly superseded by an ache near the medial portion of the homolateral zygoma and which spreads to involve a much greater area of the face including the ear.[62] Deep pains characteristically spread to be felt in areas other than those stimulated. The spread may

involve deep or superficial pathways or both. This effect
has been called "referred pain." It is attributable to the
spread of excitation in the neuraxis to other portions of
the same segment or to segments adjacent to those into
which the noxious impulses are conducted. This gives rise
to pain experience in parts innervated by deep and superficial branches of the affected segments and a variety of
motor effects.

The experience of referred pain has been studied in
the digits of the hand in human subjects. These structures
are particularly suitable for the analysis of the spread of
pain from a site of noxious stimulation because the pain
can be recognized in readily separable zones.

Accordingly, in twenty-one experiments in six subjects
it was found after immersion of one digit for 10 minutes
in water at $0°$ C, that the "cold pain" spreads from the
immersed finger to the adjacent border of the neighboring fingers on either side, and may subsequently include
the whole of a neighboring finger and part of a finger
beyond.[87]

The fifth finger was then anesthetized by a digital
block with 2 per cent procaine. The infiltration of the
paired dorsal and volar digital nerves was extended to
encircle the base of the digit and included dermis and
periosteum. The resultant sensory loss in this finger was
complete, with absence of superficial and deep pain and
of touch, temperature, position sense and vibration sense.
When the fourth finger was immersed in water, the spread
of pain to the fifth and third fingers was essentially of the
same pattern and of the same intensity as in control experiments in which the sensation of the digit was intact.
Repetition of this experiment with procaine block of the
third finger and immersion of the second in cold water
also revealed that there was no interference with the
spread of pain into the anesthetized digit. It is inferred

that: a) the spread of pain is a central rather than a peripheral effect; and b) that the spread is not dependent
upon afferent impulses from the tissue into which spread
occurs.[88] Kunkle and his associates further showed that
the spread of pain could be interrupted by preliminary
noxious stimulation of the area into which the spread
would occur. Such a maneuver also raised the cutaneous
pain threshold in the area of original stimulation and reduced the intensity of pain at that site. These experiments
are pertinent to the mechanism of pain relief by counterirritation referred to above and they support the view that
spread of pain is attributable to a central excitatory state
in the cord or higher centers which is capable of being
further excited or inhibited.

The phenomenon of "spread" has been demonstrated
in an individual who has undergone a unilateral interruption of the spinothalamic pathways below T2. Noxious
stimulation of the anesthetic half of his body induced pain
felt diffusely on the opposite side.[89] This finding illustrates
the way in which spread of excitation occurs within the
cord from impulses entering it from damaged tissue, even
though the pathways which bring to consciousness the
pain from the side stimulated have been severed (*see* Figure 7A and B). In general, the more intense the noxious
stimulation the more widespread is the area of reference.
The spread of excitation occurs by way of the neurons of
the dorsal horn and the association pathways, usually
more readily toward the head but also caudad when
the stimulus is intense. There arise in turn impulses on the
same side and on the opposite side of the cord or the
brain stem. Some of these ascend to suprasegmental
structures where neural activity is ultimately felt as
pain.[89]

SECONDARY HYPERALGESIA

The central spread of excitation also appears to give rise to a state in which afferent impulses seem more intense and persistent than they otherwise would. Thus, noxious stimulation of an area of referred pain is often productive of more discomfort than similar stimulation

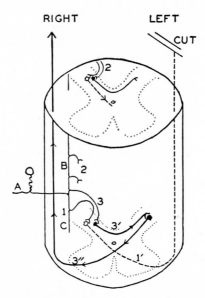

Fig. 7A. Schematic representation of the pathways for the "spread of pain" within the spinal cord. A, represents primary sensory neuron, dorsal root ganglion; B, ascending branch of the sensory radicle, and C, descending branch of the sensory radicle. 1, is a collateral to the posterior horn of the nearest spinal segment. This connects with neuron 1' which crosses to ascend in the opposite spinothalamic tract. 2, indicates collaterals to the adjacent segment, and 3, collaterals to the posterior horn connecting with neuron 3', which forms part of the posterior commissure in crossing to the opposite posterior horn, where it arborizes to connect with neuron 3"; this, in turn, crosses back to ascend the cord in the spinothalamic tract on the side of entry of the noxious impulses.

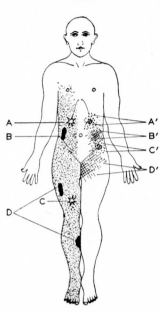

Fig. 7B. Schematic representation of the analgesia and spread of pain. The stippling shows the area of analgesia following chordotomy on the left side, approximately at the first thoraicc level. A and C are sites of noxious cutaneous stimulation of high intensity on the analgesic side; A' and C' are the diffuse areas of burning pain of low intensity perceived when areas A and C respectively were stimulated; B and D are sites of noxious stimulation of high intensity with vigorous squeezing of muscle on the analgesic side, and B' and D' are the diffuse areas of aching pain of low intensity perceived when areas B and D respectively were stimulated.

of an uninvolved region. Despite the increase in intensity of the sensation, however, threshold for cutaneous pain in the area is not altered.[88, 90] Such hyperalgesia, referred to here as secondary, may follow noxious stimulation of either superficial or deep structures. When it involves the latter it is usually spoken of as local tenderness. Another mechanism responsible for the production of local tenderness depends upon sustained contraction of muscles and will be referred to later. A demonstration of the fact that pain threshold is not altered in secondary hyperalgesia was provided by a subject who demonstrated marked hyperalgesia over the right side of the face associated with temporal arteritis. Pain threshold was the same on the two sides of the face but a stimulus above the threshold level of intensity induced one dol pain on the left cheek and forehead, but three dol pain in similar areas on the right. A stimulus productive of four dol pain on the left induced six dol pain on the right. Pain of equal intensity on the two cheeks could be induced by stimuli well above threshold and of widely differing intensity, namely 335 millicalories for three seconds on the normal left cheek and only 295 millicalories for three seconds on the hyperalgesic right cheek. Secondary hyperalgesia was experimentally induced in another subject in an area of skin at a distance from a site of repeated noxious stimulation just below the threshold for pain perception.[91, 92] Spatial summation of the effects of stimuli could be demonstrated in such a zone. Hyperalgesia was invariably promptly abolished upon withdrawal of the original noxious stimuli. These findings support the inference that secondary hyperalgesia is attributable to central neural phenomena rather than to local liberation into the skin of a chemical substance or other local change.

In an area of skin involved in a process of referred pain, not only do pain sensations arising from noxious stimulation appear intensified but so do all sensations arising from other sensory stimuli (*see* Figure 8). Another example of central reinforcement of sensory impulses other than those subserving pain is available in the case of the intensification of a light stimulus in an eye whose conjunctiva is painful because of the presence of a cinder.[93] This example also establishes that the effects of a central spread of excitation may involve not only the

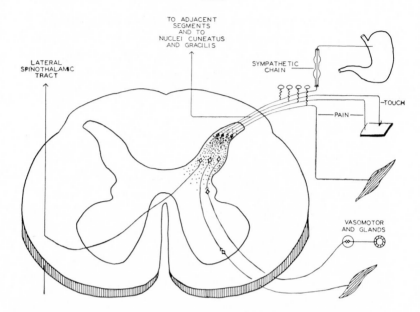

Fig. 8. Schematic representation of a spinal segment showing various effects of excitatory spread of noxious impulses from a primary noxious stimulus in the stomach. The skin becomes hyperalgesic and hyperesthetic and muscle becomes tender. Effector structures innervating blood vessels and glands (sweat and sebaceous) are involved as well as those innervating skeletal muscle causing contractions which may in themselves become painful. See also Fig. 1 Page 9.

segmental levels but also the suprasegmental, including the cerebral cortex. Visual impulses from the retina directly enter the external geniculate body. From there impulses are conveyed through secondary neurons to the cerebral cortex. Thus, as shown in Figure 9, it is not possible for neural activities involved in vision to be influenced or modified by those for pain until the latter, coming up from the brain stem through the thalamus, reach the cortex.

The hyperalgesia and hyperesthesia due to accentuation of the effects of afferent impulses arising in the tissues of a segment involved in a process of referred pain may constitute the principal element of discomfort from a given visceral disease. If that be the case local anesthetization of the superficial tissues by procaine would greatly reduce the patient's discomfort by blocking impulses arising in the skin. This effect has been noted by a variety of investigators but has been accorded undue importance as an explanation of the phenomenon of referred pain. Procainization of superficial tissues is capable of blocking stimuli arising in the anesthetized area, but not of interrupting the central spread of excitation within the cord. For example, when a tooth was noxiously stimulated, causing headache and superficial and deep hyperalgesia of the temporal region of the head, infiltration of procaine into the hyperalgesic skin and underlying soft tissues reduced but did not eliminate the headache although it did produce local analgesia. All headache was eliminated, however, by infiltration of procaine about the tooth.[94] It is therefore evident that when pain results from the persistence of the primary visceral or other deep noxious stimulation, its intensity may be modified by either superficial or deep procaine infiltration or both, but it is not eliminated until the primary afferent impulses end spontaneously or are surgically or chemically blocked at their source. Failure to recognize these relationships has given rise to misunderstandings and controversy. Now it is possible to reconcile the disparity in the findings of investigators who have injected procaine into the superficial tissues of areas of referred pain.

Not only is receptor activity involved in the spread of excitation in the nervous system but effector activity as well, as illustrated by skeletal muscle spasms, smooth muscle and gland effects shown in Figures 8 and 11, and modified reflex activity involving motility which occurs

SUPRA SEGMENTAL APPARATUS

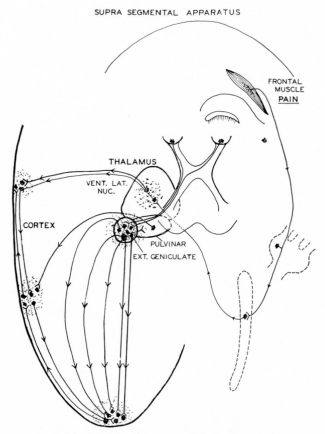

Fig. 9. Anatomic schematization of suprasegmental structures involved in the mutual intensification of noxious and light stimuli.

during painful states.[34, 95, 96] The occurrence of muscle spasms, for example, may additionally complicate the proper localization of deep pains. Noxious stimulation of the ureter has been shown to result in contraction of abdominal muscles which, when sustained, may become a source of fresh noxious impulses. At length the pain from the contracted muscles may overshadow that from the ureter (*see* Figure 10).

Such secondarily contracted muscles may also give rise to local rigidity and tenderness occurring in addition to the local tenderness attributable to the central modification of sensory impulses from an area of referred pain described above (*see* Figure 8). This dual mechanism which provides for pain and tenderness at a site remote from that of the original noxious stimulation includes another peripheral source of noxious impulses similar to that referred to above in the skin. It, too, has given rise to confusion and controversy. In this case the controversy has largely concerned whether or not the pain and tenderness in areas of referred pain can be abolished by local infiltration of muscles with procaine. From the data presented here it appears clear that pain and tenderness induced by secondary muscular spasm are modifiable by locally infiltrated procaine. When such effects predominate in the pain experience, infiltration of muscles with procaine may be effective in virtually abolishing the discomfort of visceral disease. When considerable pain is

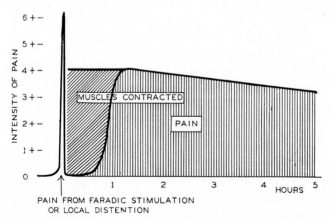

Fig. 10. Schematic representation of a sudden pain, arising from either faradic stimulation or local distention in the ureter or kidney pelvis, which was followed by contraction of skeletal muscle in which later developed an aching pain of several hours duration.

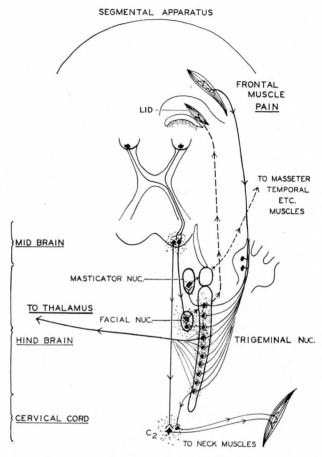

Fig. 11. Anatomic schematization of segmental structures involved in motor and sensory effects from noxious stimuli at the segmental level.

felt in situ, however, or when referred pain and tenderness are induced by a central spread of excitation involving sensory neurons, local infiltration of muscles with procaine would not be expected to modify the central effects although it would block fresh impulses arising in the periphery whose effects would become enhanced upon reaching the cord.

Widespread smooth muscle and gland effects are often coupled with the spasm and rigidity of skeletal muscles just described. Deep pain from intracranial structures, for example, is associated with contractions especially of the frontal, masseter and temporal muscles, accentuation of winking and ultimately with contraction of occipital and cervical muscles (Figure 11). These effects may be accompanied by local vasomotor changes, tearing, nasal congestion, edema of eyelids, injection of conjunctiva, sweating, pupillary dilatation, nausea and vomiting.

To epitomize this analysis it may be said that there are three categories of deep pain:

1. True Visceral and Deep Somatic Pain. Such pain is felt at the site of primary stimulation and may or may not be associated with referred pain. It is eliminated by infiltration of procaine into the site of noxious stimulation or by blocking its afferent nerves, but it is not altered by infiltration of procaine into other structures supplied by the same or adjacent neural segments (Figure 8, 9, 11).

2. Referred Pain. Such pain may occur in addition to or in the absence of the true visceral and deep somatic pain described above. It is experienced at a site other than that of stimulation but in tissues supplied by the same or adjacent neural segments. It may occur either with or without associated hyperalgesia and hyperesthesia (Figure 8).

a. Without superficial and/or deep hyperalgesia. In this case pain depends only on the central effects of the spread of excitation of the original impulses from noxious stimuli to the same and adjacent segments of the cord whence they are related to higher centers for perception and interpretation. Injection of procaine into superficial or deep regions of referred pain does not reduce the intensity of pain due to this mechanism (Figure 8).

   b. With superficial and/or deep hyperalgesia. Referred pain may be accentuated in intensity by virtue of the effects of ordinary non-noxious stimuli from zones of reference. Impulses from such sources, normally inadequate to produce pain may do so upon reaching the cord in a segment involved in central spread of excitation. Procaine injected into superficial or deep hyperalgesic structures will abolish this element of the referred pain phenomenon, resulting in more or less reduction of the subject's discomfort, depending on the amount of hyperalgesia (Figure 8). Often, when superficial hyperalgesia is a leading feature of the deep pain experience the patient may be substantially relieved by spraying ethyl chloride on the affected area of skin.

   3. Pains due to Secondary Skeletal Muscular Contractions which Provide a Fresh Source of Impulses from Noxious Stimuli. Pain may result from secondary effects of the central spread of excitation on the effector structures, including painful contractions of skeletal muscles. Such disturbances may be widespread and the pains may be experienced in situations remote from the original source of noxious stimuli. Local infiltration of the contracted muscles with procaine abolishes this type of pain by disrupting its peripheral mechanisms (Figure 8, 9, 11).

   It is suggested also: 1) that segmental phenomena within the spinal cord and brain stem account for the spread of the afferent and efferent effects associated with impulses from noxious stimulation of deep structures; 2) that localization involves conditioning, familiarity or previous experience, and, therefore, cerebral and cortical function; 3) that "hyperalgesia" and "hyperesthesia" associated with deep pain result from normal threshold impulses, and that as a result of modification within the central nervous system they are interpreted as more intense and of longer duration.

CENTRAL PAIN

So-called "central pain" is characteristic of lesions of the thalamus or spinothalamic tracts. The thalamic syndrome, as it is called, occurs most characteristically after a cerebrovascular accident in the distribution of the thalamogeniculate artery but may follow a variety of appropriately placed lesions in the thalamus, pons, medulla, cord, or even the cerebral cortex. The patient complains of constant burning and aching and dysesthesia is readily aroused. The mechanism of this phenomenon is not understood and has been little investigated, but Head and Holmes [97] have attributed it to the interruption, presumably within the thalamus, of a normally effective inhibition from cortico-thalamic impulses. An inhibitory effect has also been postulated for the rapidly conducting spinothalamic fibers.[98] It is assumed that when they are interrupted, the uninhibited impulses travelling in the slower conducting unmyelinated fibers give rise to a sensation of greater intensity than otherwise. In any case it has been demonstrated that patients with "central pain" from thalamic lesions may have an elevated threshold for the rapidly conducted pricking pain.[52] There may be a relation between this troublesome "thalamic syndrome" and causalgia and phantom limb. It appears that all of these persistent painful states depend for their mechanism upon neuronal circuits between the thalamus and cortex which can maintain a sustained state of excitation even after impulses from the periphery ordinarily inducing pain have been cut off. Also it is possible that the reticular activating system of Magoun [99] partly situated in the brain stem is important in this regard since he has shown sustained electrical activity in this area after single shocks to the sciatic or splanchnic nerves.

One of the prominent features of central pains is that their intensity is greatly accentuated when the individual is having difficulty with people and events in his daily life. Thus the mechanisms appear to be connected in the highest integrative levels to circuits carrying impulses from stimuli which owe their force to their meaning and which arise out of troublesome life situations.

It has been suggested that the intensity, duration and intractability of these "central" pain mechanisms including causalgia and phantom limb implicate the rhinencephalon and limbic systems which in turn activate autonomic responses through hypothalamic connections and whose reverberating circuits connect with the neocortex.

SENSATIONS ALLIED TO PAIN

From the studies of several investigators [100, 101, 102, 103, 104, 105, 106] it would appear that impulses which subserve the itch sensation are carried in the same fibers which are involved in the mediation of pain, not only the small non-myelinated fibers of Class C, but also in the larger more rapidly conducting myelinated fibers. The sensation of itch has two subjectively distinguishable components, one pricking and the other burning, which are mediated respectively by the myelinated and non-myelinated fibers. Cutaneous tickle does not differ qualitatively from itch, except by the addition of an awareness of movement and is mediated by the same neural structures. Itch and tickle occur when pain receptors are stimulated at intensities below the threshold for pain. Banzet has shown that intractable itching can be eliminated by section of the spinothalamic tract.[106]

Why impulses presumably carried along the same

nerve channels should give rise to qualitatively different sensations such as tickling, itching and pain is not clear. The ability to appreciate the itch sensation may depend, as Bishop [107] indicates, on a central mechanism for selective interpretation. Graham, Goodell and Wolff suggest that itch sensation results from the presence in the spinal cord of impulses traveling in circuits of internuncial neurons, with a consequent patterned discharge up the spinothalamic tracts. They found that itching in the skin could be abolished by pin prick stimulation of the skin at a distance of 30 cm. or more from the itch stimulus, but apparently in the same dermatome. Following cessation of the pin pricks there was a lag before the itch was felt again. Moreover, itch could not be produced in an area of experimentally induced hyperalgesia. Either pain or no sensation was felt.

Chapter II

PAIN ARISING FROM VARIOUS BODILY STRUCTURES

TISSUES DERIVED FROM THE ECTODERM

In GENERAL, AS HAS BEEN noted, pain may result from noxious stimulation of any structure when pain endings or peripheral fibers subserving pain exist. However, direct stimulation of the cortex of the cerebral hemispheres has predictably failed to induce pain. Even electric currents applied to the somaesthetic cortex in the post-central gyrus are not painful.* [46] On the other hand, direct stimulation of peripheral nerves which carry pain fibers is uniformly painful. Such is the mechanism of the pain of neuritis. It is commonly unremitting and has a burning quality. A disturbance of similar character, presumably related to anoxia, occurs following interruption of the circulation to an extremity. The spontaneous pain induced may be attributed to the stimulating effect of anoxia in causing the firing of impulses along pain nerves.[108] Generally, neuritis is associated with evidences of damage to the nerve including paraesthesias and sensory impairment.

Causalgia is another condition associated with burning pain and paraesthesias. It may be closely related to central pain as noted above. Its nature has never been thoroughly explained but impressions concerning the role of internuncial neurons in the mechanism of pain in causalgia, phantom limb and related states of sustained ab-

---

* Apparent exceptions in the older literature have been mentioned by White and Sweet[4] (pp. 59-60).

normal reactivity have been formulated by Livingston.[109]

Neuralgia is a term applied generally to paroxysmal pains of high intensity arising from noxious stimuli which exert their action at or near the central origin of the nerve. There is evidence to suggest that one of the most incapacitating of neuralgias, tic douloureux, may be related to anoxia from vasospasm or ischemia from other causes in the region of the Gasserian ganglion or sensory root.[110]

Tic douloureux, or trigeminal neuralgia, is a well-defined condition characterized by intermittent intense lancinating pains in the distribution of one or more of the branches of the 5th cranial nerve. Each jab of pain is only momentary although a paroxysm or volley of pains may last a matter of minutes. Between attacks the area is altogether free of pain and free of hyperalgesia. Indeed no abnormality will be detected on sensory examination. There may be numerous and frequently recurrent paroxysms of the lancinating pain lasting for hours or even days so that for the patient the suffering seems almost continuous. Attacks may be set off by almost any slight stimulus to an especially susceptible area within the affected zone. Thus, brushing the teeth, applying lipstick, or even a touch or a breeze may trigger a volley of almost unbearable pains.

Neuralgia is not ordinarily associated with loss of neural function. The term is widely misused, however, and often applied to a host of discomforts of uncertain origin about the face and head and elsewhere with and without associated hyperesthesia.

Among other tissues of ectodermal origin the skin and cornea are richly supplied with pain endings and are consequently sensitive to pain aroused by a variety of familiar stimuli. Similarly the dentine and deeper structures of the teeth are sensitive to pain.

TISSUES DERIVED FROM THE MESODERM

Erroneous inferences have been drawn that certain structures of the body are insensitive to pain when pain cannot be induced in them by stimuli commonly productive of pain in the skin, such as pricking, cutting and pinching.[34] Thus, in the case of the mesentery of the intestines or the visceral peritoneum over the spleen, scratching or cutting may not be painful while a pull from traction in the one case and rapid distention in the other may be painful. The parenchyma of lung and liver have been thought to be devoid of nerves capable of transmitting painful impulses because they may be cut and pinched during operations without inducing pain in the conscious patient. This evidence, however, as indicated, does not necessarily allow for such a sweeping inference. The adequacy of a stimulus may depend not only on its type but on the state of the tissue stimulated. The effects of engorgement and inflammation of tissues on their pain thresholds have been discussed.

Most tissues of mesodermal origin are supplied with pathways which conduct painful impulses, notably the subcutaneous structures, ligaments, tendons and muscles. The periosteum of bone is sensitive as is the cancellous portion, but existing evidence indicates that the cortex and marrow cavities of long bones are not equipped with receptors for pain. Fascia, ligaments, articular capsules and synoviae have been found to be sensitive to pain but not the articular cartilage.[111] These structures are often implicated in pains which occur after sudden reduction in atmospheric pressure as in decompression or altitude sickness. In the latter condition nitrogen bubbles have been demonstrated in the vascular system, and synovial fluid of joints.[112, 113] In the case of skeletal muscle, cutting pricking and pinching are less painful than when applied to the skin. Chemical irritants injected into muscles may give rise to considerable pain but the usual ways in which pain in the intact body arises from muscles are in association with stretching, ischemia or unduly forceful or sustained contractile activity.[34, 50] In both of the latter cases there is some evidence that the nerve endings may be stimulated by an excessive concentration of potassium.[114] It has been shown that a large proportion of headaches, especially those accompanied by stiffness or tenderness in the neck and occipital region find their origin in unduly sustained increase of the contractile state of underlying head and neck muscles.[95] Ischemia of these muscles is also relevant to the pain induced by contraction. It is likely that a similar mechanism explains many backaches. Ischemia of muscles induces the pain in the extremities in intermittent claudication and occlusive vascular disease and is the basis of the pain of coronary occlusion.[115]

In the chest, the visceral pleura is insensitive to pain while the parietal pleura is richly supplied with pain endings through the intercostal nerves, and, on the diaphragmatic surface, by the phrenic nerve as well.[116] The lower portion of the fibrous pericardium appears to be supplied by pain fibers from the phrenic nerve. Elsewhere and throughout their serous surfaces the visceral and parietal pericardia are insensitive to pain.

Other mesodermal structures frequently concerned with the mediation of pain are the blood vessels. Distortion of cranial vessels by pulling, displacement or distention have been found to be the source of a large proportion of headaches including migraine, the headache associated with arterial hypertension, the headaches of brain tumor and headaches associated with variations in the hydro-dynamics of the cerebrospinal fluid.[117] There is also evidence that blood vessels may be implicated in the pain induced by cold.[17]

TISSUES DERIVED FROM THE ENDODERM

In regard to pain arising from endodermal structures some confusion has existed because, although pains occurring from disturbances along the course of the gastrointestinal tract are commonly met with in medical practice, efforts to induce them by deliberate stimulation have not always been successful. The larger arteries of the mesenteries themselves and the parietal peritoneum are pain-sensitive, as noted above. The wall of the gut itself, however from mucosa to serosa, has been thought to be insensitive to pain because it has been cut, burned and crushed in the conscious subject without complaint of pain. Present evidence indicates that such conclusions are premature and that under appropriate circumstances both the mucosa and deeper structures of the gut are sensitive to pain.[64] Moreover, the musocal linings of the urethra, bladder, ureters and kidney pelvis have been shown to be sensitive to pain.[66]

PAIN FROM VARIOUS SEGMENTAL LEVELS

Pain from the Head

The head provides the site of origin of a large proportion of pains which afflict mankind. Therefore headaches of various types will be considered in detail together with the mechanisms responsible for them.[117, 118, 119]

The sensitivity to pain of the tissues covering the cranium, the cranium itself and most of the intracranial structures, has been ascertained from a series of patients during surgical procedures on the head.[46]

Application of faradic current, traction, pinching and other stimuli has resulted in the following conclusions about the sensitivity to pain of the structures investigated:

1. Of the tissues covering the cranium, all were more or less sensitive to pain, the arteries being especially so.

2. Of the intracranial structures, the great venous sinuses and their venous tributaries from the surface of the brain, parts of the pia and dura at the base, the dural arteries and the large cerebral arteries at the base of the brain, the fifth, ninth and tenth cranial nerves, and the upper three cervical nerves were sensitive to pain.

3. The cranium (including the diploic and emissary veins), the parenchyma of the brain, most of the dura, most of the pia arachnoid, the ependymal lining of the ventricles and the choroid plexuses, were not sensitive to pain.

Stimulation of the pain-sensitive intracranial structures on or above the superior surface of the tentorium cerebelli resulted in pain in various regions in front of a line drawn vertically from the ears across the top of the head. The pathways for this pain are contained in the fifth cranial nerve.

Stimulation of the pain-sensitive intracranial structures on or below the inferior surface of the tentorium cerebelli resulted in pain in various regions behind the line just described. The pathways for this pain are contained chiefly in the ninth and tenth cranial nerves and the upper three cervical nerves.

The ophthalmic, maxillary and mandibular branches of the trigeminal or fifth cranial nerve are mainly concerned with mediating pain from the face, nasal structures, nasopharynx, and mouth, and are distributed fan-wise over the face and front of the head. The upper, or ophthalmic branch supplies the anterior aspect of the nose, eyes, forehead, and head as far back as the line mentioned which extends over the dome and connects the ears. The head behind this region is supplied by branches of the second and possibly the first cervical segments. The second, or maxillary branch of the trigeminal nerve supplies the zygomatic region, the remainder of the nose and upper lip. The lower, or mandibular branch supplies the remainder of the face as far down as the margin of the mandibular ramus. Below this line the face is supplied by the third cervical segment. The facial or seventh cranial nerve may carry noxious impulses from some of the muscles, arteries and other deeper structures of the face. Impulses from noxious stimuli from the pharynx, tonsillar pillars and fossae are carried in the glossopharyngeal, or ninth cranial nerve.

The ear is unique in that there is no other structure in the body of comparable size that is supplied by sensory nerves from so many neural segments. Because the ear is supplied by twigs from the fifth, seventh, ninth and tenth cranial nerves and the scalp and muscles in its immediate vicinity by branches from the upper cervical roots, noxious stimuli from regions of the head remote from it commonly cause pain to be experienced in the ear.

From the data available, six basic mechanisms of headache from intracranial sources have been formulated. Headache may result from: 1) traction on the veins that pass to the venous sinuses from the surface of the brain and displacement of the great venous sinuses; 2) traction on the middle meningeal arteries; 3) traction on the large arteries at the base of the brain and their main branches; 4) distention and dilatation of intracranial arteries; 5) inflammation in or about any of the pain sensitive structures of the head, and 6) direct pressure by tumors on the cranial and cervical nerves containing many afferent fibers from the head.

Intracranial diseases commonly cause headache through more than one of these mechanisms and by involvement of more than one pain sensitive structure. Traction, displacement, distention and inflammation of cranial vascular structures are chiefly responsible for headache.

Headache from intracranial disease is usually referred pain. Local tenderness of the scalp may prove useful as an index to the structures responsible when a lesion produces direct irritation of pain-sensitive structures. Disease of two or more remotely separated pain-sensitive structures may, however, cause pain and hyperalgesia in identical areas. Pains in the head have not been encountered as phenomena of reference from structures outside the head and neck except when pain occurs in the jaw with angina pectoris. Occipital headache and even pain in the eye may arise from branches of the vertebral arteries innervated by the upper cervical segments.[120] The muscles which attach to the skull are also a prominent source of headache as will be discussed below.

Headache Associated with Changes in Intracranial Pressure. Normal human subjects, having been subjected to the removal of cerebrospinal fluid through a lumbar needle, were placed on a tilt table in various planes from horizontal to vertical while measurements were made of the hydrodynamics of the remaining spinal fluid.[121] It was found that headache was regularly induced in the erect position by the free drainage of approximately 20 cc. of cerebrospinal fluid (about 10 per cent of total intra-cranio-spinal contents). During this procedure the estimated pressure at the vertex of the cranium fell from a normal level of approximately minus 150 mm. to between minus 220 and minus 290 mm.

Drainage headache was reduced in intensity by the intrathecal injection of sufficient saline to restore the normal volume of cerebrospinal fluid. It was also reduced in intensity by body tilting toward the horizontal or simply by head flexion or extension. In its response to postural changes, drainage headache was shown to be independent of the estimated intracranial pressure. On the other hand, drainage headache was usually augmented in intensity during distention of intracranial veins secondary to bilateral jugular compression. The afferent impulses respon-

sible for pain in the front of the head in headache from
drainage traverse chiefly the fifth cranial nerve.

It was thus inferred that drainage headache is caused
primarily by traction by the brain upon various pain-
sensitive structures which anchor it to the cranium. Dilatation of some of these structures, such as the intracranial
veins, and increase in brain volume appear to operate as
joint factors in augmenting the displacement of pain-
sensitive structures which follows drainage of fluid and
leads to headache.

The headache which often follows lumbar puncture
was found to have certain predictable and unique features,
all of which indicate its similarity to the drainage headache. Like drainage headache, post-puncture headache
was associated with a decrease in cerebrospinal fluid volume as evidenced by a fall in cerebrospinal pressure. It
was completely eliminated by the intrathecal injection of
saline and elevation of intracranial pressure to normal.
Its intensity was reduced by change from the erect to
the horizontal position or by head flexion or extension; its
intensity was increased by bilateral jugular compression.

The usual variety of post-puncture headache is, therefore, similar in type and mechanism to the headache induced by drainage of cerebrospinal fluid, i.e., it is caused
by dilatation of and traction upon pain-sensitive intracranial vascular structures. It is probably secondary to a prolonged leakage of fluid through the dural hole in the
lumbar sac produced by the operator's needle. "Sterile
meningitis" was found to be an uncommon cause of post-
puncture headache.

The headache so often associated with increased intracranial pressure has generally been assumed, but never
proven, to be directly attributable to the increased pressure. Experimentally it was found that elevation of intracranial pressure in normal human subjects to unusually

high levels failed to cause headache.[121] Headache homo-lateral to the lesion in a patient with a brain tumor was induced by lowering the intracranial pressure, but could not be induced by elevation of the pressure to a high level of 550 mm.

Hence, in the production of headache, increased intra-cranial pressure is neither a prime nor an essential factor.

From these data it is concluded that the headache associated with either decreased or increased intracranial pressure results from traction upon or displacement of pain-sensitive intracranial structures and is independent of generalized intracranial pressure changes per se.

Brain Tumor Headache. It was further evident from an analysis of the record of seventy-two patients [122] that increased intracranial pressure is not the dominant factor in headache associated with brain tumor since 1) head-ache occurred almost as commonly (82 per cent) in twenty-three patients without increased intracranial pres-sure as it did (94 per cent) in forty-nine patients with in-creased pressure. 2) The reduction of elevated pressure did not inevitably eliminate brain tumor headache. 3) At surgical operation the headache could be reproduced ex-perimentally by distortion of pain-sensitive structures adjacent to the tumor.

Brain tumor headache is produced by traction upon intracranial pain-sensitive structures, chiefly the larger arteries, veins and venous sinuses, and certain cranial nerves. There are two types of traction which operate singly or in combination: 1) local traction by the tumor upon adjacent structures; and 2) traction by virtue of more or less remote disturbances such as extensive dis-placement of the brain either directly by the tumor, or indirectly by ventricular obstruction (internal hydro-cephalus). Headache was found to be of considerable aid in the localization of brain tumors when it was interpreted in terms of known principals of production and reference of intracranial pain.

In general, from studies of patients with brain tumor the following generalizations concerning headache as an aid to localization seem justified.

1. Although the headache of brain tumor is often referred from a distant intracranial source, it approximately overlies the tumor in about 50 per cent of all patients.

2. Brain tumor headache in the absence of papilledema is of great localizing value. In about two-thirds of such patients the headache immediately overlies or is near the tumor and in all, when unilateral, it is on the same side as the tumor.

3. Headache is almost always present with posterior fossa tumor.

4. Headache may be absent with any of the common types of supratentorial tumor.

5. The headache of posterior fossa tumor is almost always over the back of the head, although it may occur elsewhere as well.

6. Headache is usually the first symptom of posterior fossa tumor except in the cerebello-pontine angle.

7. Headache is the first symptom of one-third of supratentorial tumors.

8. The headache of cerebello-pontine angle tumors is frequently and sometimes solely post-auricular, and homolateral.

9. Headache from supratentorial tumors is rarely in the back of the head, unless associated with papilledema.

10. When supratentorial tumors cause headache in the back of the head, headache in the front of the head is usually also present.

11. When headache is both frontal and occipital it

indicates extensive displacement of the brain and has little localizing value.

12. Brain tumor headache is usually intermittent, but when it is continuous its value in localization is greatly enhanced.

For bedside purposes, an epitome of the above considerations is as follows: In spite of these limitations the headache of brain tumor may aid significantly in the localization of the lesion, especially when the headache is continuous. Thus, generally speaking, a) in the absence of papilledema, when the headache is one sided the side of the headache is usually the side of the tumor; b) with tumor of the posterior fossa the headache is initially in the back of the head; c) with tumor above the tentorium, in the absence of papilledema, the headache is usually in the front of the head; d) when headache is both frontal and occipital it is without localizing value. But often the history of the headache—whether it was initially on the left or the right, frontal or occipital, may indicate the site of the lesion.

Headache Experimentally Induced by Histamine. Simultaneous recording of the systemic arterial blood pressure, the cerebrospinal fluid pressure, the temporal artery pulsations and the intracranial pulsations led to the conclusion that headache following intravenous injection of histamine resulted mainly from the dilatation and distention of cerebral arteries.[123] Such histamine headaches were abolished by increasing the intracranial pressure, thereby giving extramural support to the cerebral arteries at the base of the brain.

By experiments with local anesthesia it was shown that histamine headache does not depend upon the integrity of sensation from the superficial tissues. Although there may be other less important afferent pathways for the conduction of impulses interpreted as headache following injection of histamine, the fifth cranial nerve on each side is the principal afferent pathway for headache resulting from dilatation of the supratentorial cerebral arteries and felt in the fronto-temporo-parietal region of the head, and the ninth and tenth cranial and upper cervical nerves are the most important afferent pathways for headache resulting from dilatation of the arteries of the posterior fossa and felt in the occipital region of the head.

Headache Associated with Fever Sepsis and Bacteremia. Similar study of headache associated with experimentally induced fever showed that, like the histamine headache, its intensity varied with changes in the amplitude of pulsations of the cerebrospinal fluid.[124] Furthermore, like histamine headache, the headache associated with fever could be relieved by increasing the cerebrospinal fluid pressure in the subarachnoid space.

Migraine Headache. In contrast to the headaches of histamine and fever, changes in the intensity of the migraine headache are related to changes in the amplitude of pulsations of chiefly the branches of the external carotid arteries.[45] Factors which decrease the amplitude of pulsations were found to decrease the intensity of the headache. Thus, it has been shown by means of observations and photographic recordings made both before and during the action of ergotamine tartrate, that this agent reduces the amplitude of pulsations of the aforementioned arteries by about 50 per cent, and thereby diminishes the intensity of or terminates the migraine headache. Reduction in the amplitude of pulsations of the temporal artery by digital pressure on the carotid artery on the affected side was also accompanied by reduction in the intensity of the headache. Conversely, experimental distention of extracranial arteries in the absence of headache resulted in pain.

There is some evidence that the pial and cerebral arteries contribute to the pain of the migraine headache since faradic stimulation of the proximal few centimeters of the anterior, middle and posterior cerebral arteries and the first few centimeters of the intracranial portion of the internal carotid artery causes pain within, behind or over the homolateral eye. Furthermore, stimulation of the vertebral and basilar arteries and the proximal portions of their branches causes pain in the occipital and suboccipital region. These areas are commonly involved in migraine attacks. Moreover, persons familiar with the experience of migraine headache often note that headache induced by histamine resembles the most intense of their attacks of migraine. Since it was not possible to reduce the intensity of even some of the worst attacks of migraine headache by raising the cerebrospinal fluid pressure as high as 800 mm. of water, however, it appears that the pial and cerebral arteries are not the major contributors to the pain.

Although most attacks of migraine headache are limited to the temporal, the frontal or the occipital region, some patients have pain elsewhere. In the face, below the eye, and behind and below the zygoma, severe throbbing pain which seems to emanate from the back teeth of the upper jaw, occasionally occurs. Another variant is facial pain, which spreads behind the angle of the jaw, down the neck and into the shoulder. The latter aching sensations are sometimes associated with awareness of unusual throbbing in the neck.

The pains described can and probably do result from dilatation and distention of the extracranial portion of the middle meningeal artery, between its origin and the point

of entrance into the skull, the internal maxillary artery and
the trunks of the external and the common carotid artery.
It has been shown that the latter structures are sensitive
to pain and the sites in which pain is felt are the face,
neck and shoulder.

Headaches Associated with Arterial Hypertension.
Studies made of the headache associated with hypertension by the methods outlined above have revealed that
essentially the same mechanism is operative in producing
this pain as in producing the migraine headache.[124] It is
to be emphasized that this statement applies not to the
so-called hypertensive encephalopathy of Fishberg,[125] or
"hypertensive crisis," but rather to the frequent, severe
and often incapacitating headaches suffered by hypertensive patients who may otherwise be free of symptoms.
The term "hypertensive headache" is misleading, since
it implies that the frequency and severity of the headache
are directly related to the level of the blood pressure. It
has been shown that the headache in subjects with hypertension bears no direct relationship to the level of blood
pressure or pulse pressure. The headache may be present
when the blood pressure is relatively high, moderate or
low. By pressing the thumb upon the common carotid
artery the intensity of the headache was reduced with an
accompanying decline in the amplitude of the pulsation.
Decrease in the intensity of headache in the temporal
region followed similar pressure upon the corresponding
temporal artery. Furthermore, when ergotamine tartrate
appreciably decreased the amplitude of pulsations of the
cranial arteries, the intensity of the "hypertensive" headache decreased despite the fact that the ergotamine tartrate considerably increased the already elevated systolic
and diastolic pressures.

The fact that the high level of blood pressure among
hypertensive subjects is not a sufficient condition for

headache does not justify the assumption that these phenomena are unrelated. Indeed, this too, would be contradicted by the facts of common experience, since some persons with hypertension never had headache until the hypertension became established. It is apparently the arterioles that are implicated in the mechanism of hypertension and the arteries in the mechanism of headache. Headache can occur when the artery walls themselves are in a relatively lax state and capable of being distended or when the force of the blood pulsing through is greatly increased. Actually the same blood pressure is capable of exerting more tension on the blood vessel enclosing it when the vessel's diameter is relatively large than when it is constricted. This principle is contained in the formulas of Laplace which relate the tension on the wall of a container to the pressure within. In keeping with these formulas the tension on the wall of a blood vessel would depend not only on the pressure of the blood within but upon the diameter of the vessel itself: the wider the vessel the greater the tension.

The operation of the law can be simply illustrated by blowing into a sausage-shaped toy balloon. When it is half blown up the center is fat and very taut while the far end is loose and very little inflated. The actual pressure throughout the interior of the balloon is the same, in keeping with Pascal's law which states that the pressure of a gas in a closed space is equal in every direction. The tension on the balloon itself, however, is greatest in the region where its internal diameter is greatest. Thus the tension on an artery's wall is greater when it is dilated than when it is constricted, even though the blood pressure within is the same. A further factor which can increase the tension within the wall of an artery is turgor of the artery itself. This swelling may occur after damage to the vessel or after prolonged stretching, as with a headache.

Similarly, in experimental histamine headache, the headache and maximal distention of the cranial arteries occur not immediately after the injection of histamine, when the effect on the contractile state of these vessels is greatest, but some time later, when the blood pressure returns to its initial level. It is at this time that the walls of the cranial arteries react to the mounting pressure and headache becomes associated with a level of blood pressure which is ordinarily associated with comfort. The relaxation of arterial walls is thus seen to be one necessary factor in the production of histamine headache, and the level of the blood pressure the other. The analogy to the circumstances in hypertension is close. During an average or normal contractile state of the arterial walls, distention does not occur, and, correspondingly, there is no headache; but should this contractile state be impaired, as during periods of stress, fatigue, or other conditions, distention and headache follows. In brief, high blood pressure is a necessary but not a sufficient condition for this type of headache. There is a significant relation between headache associated with hypertension and the contractile state of the cranial arteries.

"Constipation Headache." Robertson and co-workers [126] attempted to induce headache by mechanical distention of the rectum. This maneuver did not induce headache in intact subjects even in those in whom headaches were a common occurrence. Thus it seems clear that distention of the rectum by feces cannot explain "constipation headache." In human subjects with cord transections at T7 or above, however, Schumacher [127] was able to induce a vascular headache by distention of either the rectum or bladder. The mechanism thus did not depend upon a direct neural reflex but upon the intervention of autonomic effects which included elevation of arterial pressure and relaxation with painful distention of cranial arteries. Presumably in the intact subjects this chain of events was interrupted by inhibitory impulses from above.

General Observations Concerning Vascular Headaches. Kunkle and his co-workers [128] have demonstrated two phenomena common to vascular headaches which support the foregoing inferences concerning their mechaism. These headaches could be induced or accentuated by effecting a pull upon intracranial vascular attachments by subjecting the head to a rotary jolt in the horizontal plane. Moreover, headaches originating from distention of cranial vessels were abolished when human beings were centrifuged so that the blood was spun out of their cranial vessels.

Headache from Sustained Contraction of Skeletal Muscle. A most frequently encountered headache mechanism is that occurring in association with sustained skeletal muscle contraction. The involved muscles are those which insert on the scalp, chiefly the large neck muscles which attach to the vertex and occipital region. Sustained contraction of these structures, associated as it often is with feelings of conflict and emotional tension gives rise to pain but pain of lower intensity than that associated with vascular headache mechanisms. Muscle tension headaches, however, are often more persistent and frequently recurrent. Direct myographic tracings made from head and neck muscles during such headaches have shown significant local increase in muscle potential.[95]

There is a good deal of evidence that a local reduction in blood supply to the muscles contributes to the mechanism of pain from muscle tightness. Recordings from branches of the temporal artery during such headaches reveal a sharp decrease in the amplitude of pulsation and evidence of increased resistance to flow.[129] Also the inspection of the bulbar conjunctival vessels reveals ischemia on the side of the headache.[130]

Tightness of muscles productive of headache may occur not only in association with conscious or unconscious emotional tension but also in association with sustained concentration or effort requiring, for example, prolonged use of the eyes. Thus headache from tightness of the scalp muscles is frequently wrongly attributed to ocular disturbances. Another mechanism for painful tightness in scalp muscles may derive from inflammation in the head, especially in the paranasal sinuses. Here the efferent nerves to the muscles carry impulses resulting from the central excitatory state set up by afferent impulses from the inflamed area as described on page 35.

Headache Associated with Disease of the Nasal and Paranasal Structures; the "Sinus Headache." The mucosal lining of the paranasal sinuses themselves displayed a relatively low order of sensitivity compared to the nasal mucosa and especially the ostia of the sinuses which were actuely sensitive. Headaches of the "sinus" type do not necessarily imply sinus disease. Inflammatory change or other noxious stimulation limited to the nose produced headaches of the typical "sinus" variety. Similarly, headaches associated with sinus disease were found to be of little localizing value. Stimulation of widely separated structures in the nose and paranasal region gave rise to pain originating near the medial border of the zygoma and spreading widely over the face and head.

Pain in the back of the head or neck never resulted directly from stimulation of the mucosa of any of the nasal or paranasal structures. Such pain was due to the secondary effects of prolonged contraction of the cervical and head muscles as described above.

Pain Arising from the Eye and Ocular Disorders. The structures within the orbits of healthy subjects and patients with eye disease were stimulated by a variety of methods.[93] It was learned that most headaches associated with visual disturbances do not arise in the ocular structures themselves but from increased contractile state of the muscles of the head in association with the tension and distress which commonly accompanies difficulty with vision. Pain may arise, however, from traction on the extraocular muscles or from the ciliary muscle and iris. Elevation of intraocular pressure is an important cause of pain in the eye and when this pressure was sufficiently high, pain radiated over the entire distribution of the ophthalmic division of the trigeminal nerve and was often accompanied by nausea. Photophobia was found to depend on either of two mechanisms. In subjects with diseased irides the constriction of the muscles of the iris induced by the light stimulus caused painful traction upon the structures which had lost their mobility. This type of photophobia could invariably be relieved by mydriasis despite the fact that such a procedure admitted more light to the eye. The second mechanism for photophobia as referred to in the analysis of deep pain was found to depend upon noxious stimulation of end organs of the ophthalmic branch of the trigeminal nerve as well as the light stimulus. Vascular congestion was apparently not a factor. Such photophobia could regularly be relieved by surface anaesthesia but not by mydriasis or cycloplegia. Photophobia could not be induced in the presence of the Argyll-Robertson pupil.

PAIN FROM SEGMENTS BELOW THE HEAD

Below the head, the sites where painful sensations are felt bear a more readily recognizable segmental relationship to the sites stimulated. For the skin and the supporting structures, this distribution is well known and localization of pain from noxious stimuli is sharp. The distribution on the body is in belt-like strips arranged obliquely, higher posteriorly over the spine and lower anteriorly over the chest and abdomen. The neck and region above the clavicle are supplied by C3. The slope of the shoulders and region anteriorly just beneath the clavicle are supplied by C4. Segments C5 to T1 are concerned with the supply of the shoulders and upper extremities. This more complex distribution is illustrated in Figure 12 and 13. The thoracic segments supply areas on the body below that indicated for C4. There is considerable overlapping of ramifying branches but the following landmarks serve as useful orientation for the distribution of the various segments. T4 supplies the area in which would fall a line drawn along the fifth rib to the midsternum through the nipples. T10 supplies an area in which would fall a line drawn along the twelfth rib and extended through the umbilicus. T12 extends from the flank region in back anteriorly along Poupart's ligament. Among these various landmarks lie in orderly fashion the areas of distribution of the other thoracic segments. The lumbar and sacral segments are concerned with supplying the lower extremities and perineum. These more complex distributions are illustrated in Figures 14 and 15.

The segmental distribution for the deeper structures including muscles, ligaments and periosteum differs from that in the skin mainly in the extremities and the region of the shoulders and pelvic girdle. Here, in the region of the angle of the scapula, for example, periosteum, tendons and muscles are innervated by the 7th cervical segment while the overlying skin is supplied by branches from seven or more segments below, namely T6-T9. (*See* Figure 13). Elsewhere the segmental innervation is arranged approximately as that in the overlying skin. From most viscera, however, afferent impulses travel into the cord over a large number of roots which may be remote from the viscus itself. Thus, several segments may be involved. Data concerning pathways for noxious impulses from viscera have come mainly from studies involving surgical interruption of the impulses either in the sympathetic chains, the dorsal roots or in the cord. The visceral contents of the abdominal cavity can be made pain insensitive by resection of the sympathetic ganglionated chain from the stellate through the third lumbar. These sizable nerves contain half autonomic (efferent) fibers and half sensory (afferent) fibers. Some of the organs are innervated unilaterally but most have bilateral innervation. Much confusion could be eliminated if it were appreciated that sympathectomy within the abdominal cavity is always de-afferentation as well. Section of the

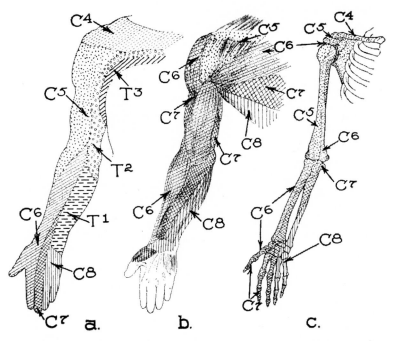

Fig. 12. Dermatomes and sclerotomes of the upper extremity: a) skin, b) muscles and c) skeletal structures in front view (Inman and Saunders).[131]

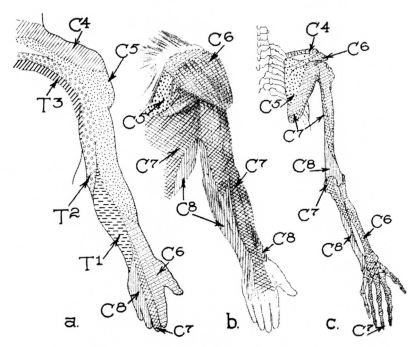

Fig. 13. Dermatomes and sclerotomes of the upper extremity: a) skin, b) muscles and c) skeletal structures in rear view (Inman and Saunders).[131] Compare with Figure 10 and note the discrepancy in innervation of deep and superficial structures over posterior chest.

sympathetic fibers for abdominal pain presents the advantage of specific organ analgesia without involving peritoneal, muscle, or skin sensation.

The emphasis on the referral of deep pain to skin segments has given rise to confusion and a lack of awareness that deep pain from skeleton or viscera may be felt in situ and may be referred along the distribution of the deep branches of a segmental nerve and not be felt in the skin at all. Inman and Saunders [131] have emphasized this fact in explaining the paths of reference of pain arising

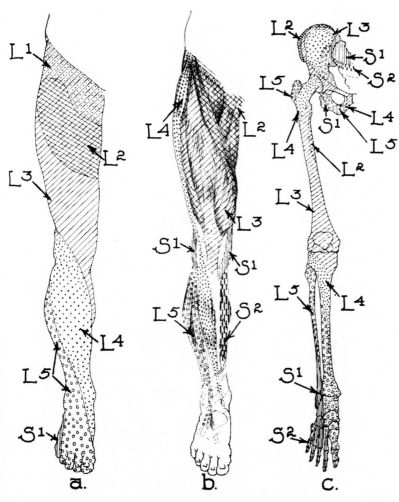

Fig. 14. Dermatomes and sclerotomes of the lower extremity: a) skin, b) muscles and c) skeletal structures in front view (Inman and Saunders).[131]

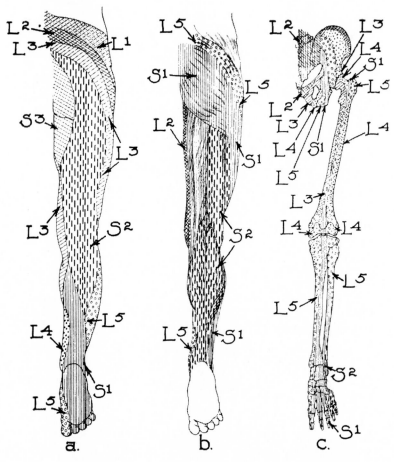

Fig. 15. Dermatomes and sclerotomes of the lower extremity: a) skin, b) muscles and c) skeletal structures in rear view (Inman and Saunders).[131]

from the various lesions of the skeleton which have always seemed confusing when one thinks of pain distribution exclusively in terms of cutaneous segments.

Cutaneous segments, of course, are commonly involved in deep pain and may provide the most prominent site of pain. The fact that a referred pain actually involves a cutaneous segment is most readily identified by the presence of hyperalgesia already referred to.

Another source of confusion among those concerned with identification of various pains has been failure fully to realize the fact that a referred pain need not involve the whole segment of reference.[66] In fact it usually does not. Most pains arising from disease in abdominal viscera are felt anteriorly on the abdomen in the ventral part of the segment concerned. Ureteral pain is first felt anteriorly, and posteriorly in the flanks only when the stimulus is intense. Pain from the kidney pelvis a few millimeters away, however, is characteristically first felt at the costovertebral angle. Pain from noxious stimulation of the gall bladder may be felt only posteriorly at the angle of the scapula in one portion of the ninth thoracic segment. Thus pains from deep structures may be felt in situ and often fairly well localized. They may be referred along the deep distribution of spinal nerves or along their cutaneous distribution or both. Reference occurs most readily first to other parts of the same segment; next to adjacent segments higher in the cord; next to adjacent segments lower down and finally to corresponding segments on the opposite side of the cord without ever involving the whole of the original segment.[132] Disease of specific organs of the body often gives rise to a pattern of distribution of pain which is characteristic of that organ. Why noxious impulses from several structures innervated by the same segments are referred along more or less characteristic pathways involving specific parts of the segments is not clear but it is probably related to experience. We are generally more conscious of the front half of our body than the rear and we are especially conscious of parts which customarily receive noxious stimuli from the outside such as the precordium and epigastrium. It is logical to expect that these parts of the thoracic segments would be most involved in painful experiences. Similarly in the head the eye is prominently involved in painful syndromes since the eye is a structure which is continually exposed to noxious stimuli and concerned with eliminating particles of dust and other foreign bodies.

Bone Pain. Bone pains are among the most troublesome discomforts with which the clinician must deal. They occur most characteristically when bones are softened by osteoporosis or by neoplastic infiltration. The mechanism of bone pain has never been thoroughly explained but the circumstances seem to fit best with the hypothesis of structural stress. When supporting bony structures are weakened by loss of calcium and protein matrix pain accompanies such stresses as weight bearing. In the treatment of painful osseous metastases by chemical agents it has repeatedly been observed that mitigation of pain intensity goes hand in hand with reduction of urinary calcium excretion. In general, greater degrees of urinary calcium loss are indicative of increasing intensity of pain.

Cardiac Pain. Impulses from noxious stimuli from the heart travel in company with sympathetic nerves, entering the sympathetic chains anywhere from the middle cervical to the fifth thoracic ganglion. Here the fibers may travel up or down in the chain but enter the cord in the upper five thoracic roots [29] (*See* Figure 16). Characteristically pain from the heart is felt in situ beneath the sternum. Referred pain to the surface is localized mainly in the anterior portion of thoracic segments 3-6 with hyperesthesia involving the precordial area, and along the medial aspect of the left shoulder and arm in the distribution of T1 and 2. The area of reference of cardiac pain may, however, extend over a wider path of reference from C3 to T10.[26, 29] Thus, it may be confused with pain arising from noxious stimulation of other structures innervated by the

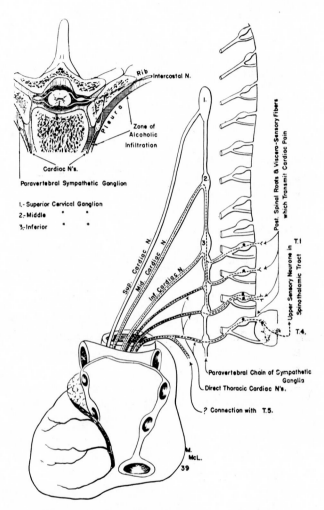

Fig. 16. Afferent nerve pathways for heart and location of paravertebral sympathetic ganglia (J. C. White).[29]

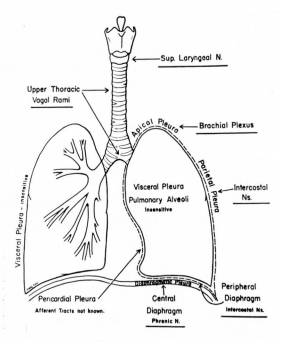

Fig. 17. Afferent nerve pathways for respiratory tree and pleural
surfaces (J. C. White).[29]

same segment notably the biliary passages, diaphragm,
mediastinum, esophagus, apex of the lung, spinal cord,
nerve roots and skeletal and muscular structures about
the left shoulder and chest. When cardiac pain reaches
to the lower jaw it may suggest disease of the apices of
the lower teeth.

Pain which simulates that of cardiac origin may derive
from contraction of the muscles of the chest. Such
"pseudo-angina" if often located to the left of the typical
substernal site of heart pain. Disturbances in numerous
other structures including the esophagus, diaphragm, gall
bladder, pancreas, stomach, small intestine and colon

may simulate heart pain.[133] The syndrome of the splenic flexure is particularly striking in this regard.[134] Here distention of the first portion of the descending colon, especially when redundant, causes pain in the chest.

Pleuropericardial Pain. The visceral pleura is apparently not a pain-sensitive structure. From the parietal pleura noxious impulses reach the cord via the intercostal nerves and hence pains are felt in the area of the cutaneous segment immediately overlying the site of stimulation.[29] This is true also of the portion of the parietal pleura reflected over the peripheral border of the diaphragm. (*See* Figure 17.) Posteriorly, where a considerable extent of the diaphragm lies against the chest wall, pains from noxious stimulation of its pleural surface may be felt in parts of thoracic segments 7-12 including the lower thorax, lumbar region, epigastrium and even further down in the abdomen. Capps [116] has described the occurrence of pain in the right lower quadrant of the abdomen with localized tenderness, cutaneous hyperesthesia in the region of McBurney's point, and spasm of underlying muscles in diaphragmatic pleurisy complicating pneumonia.

Noxious stimulation of the central portion of the diaphragmatic pleura which is supplied by branches of the phrenic nerve gives rise to pain in the region of the trapezius muscle in the neck and shoulder, the cutaneous distribution of the third and fourth cervical segments of the cord.

Phrenic nerve endings also supply the lower portion of the parietal pericardium and thus noxious stimulation of this membrane also causes pain in the trapezius region. Noxious stimuli applied to the parietal pericardium at a distance from the diaphragm, however, do not induce pain. Neither has the visceral pericardium been found to be pain sensitive. The frequent association of pain in the chest with certain types of pericarditis has been ascribed to noxious stimuli reaching the pleural surfaces adjacent to the pericardium.

Pulmonary and Diaphragmatic Pain. The lungs and bronchi originate embryologically as outpouchings from the primitive gut tube in the neck and are hence innervated by fibers from the third and fourth cervical segments which are carried in the vagal rami to the cord.[29] Sensations arising from noxious stimulation of these structures are not necessarily referred to the cervical region, however, and are often correctly localized. Thus, in tracheitis the pain is felt beneath the sternum and in centrally located bronchogenic carcinomata pain may be felt in the chest immediately overlying the lesion. Noxious impulses from the diaphragm travel mainly in the phrenic nerve, entering the cord in the third, fourth, and fifth cervical roots. The peripheral portion of the diaphragm receives fibers from intercostal nerves and thus, as in the case of its pleural surface, noxious stimulation of the muscle near its insertion will give rise to pain felt in the thoracic segments. Areas of reference for pain in the diaphragm may extend as far down over the abdomen and lumbar region as T12. Indeed the pain of coronary occlusion has been closely simulated by diaphragmatic spasm.[135]

Gastrointestinal Pain. General Statement: Like the head, the gastrointestinal tract is responsible for a large proportion of the painful afflictions of man. In the gastrointestinal tract noxious impulses arise principally from one or more of three sources, 1) local noxious stimulation of an engorged or inflamed mucosa, 2) distention or spasm of muscular elements of the tube and 3) traction upon mesenteric attachments.

Esophagus: From the esophagus noxious impulses are thought to travel in fibers carried by the sympathetic nerves to the chains of sympathetic ganglia. From here they may enter the cord anywhere from the lowest cervical through the entire thoracic distribution. (*See* Figure 18.) Whether or not the vagus participates in carrying afferent fibers which relay noxious impulses and pain is still unsettled.[29] The commonest pain from the esophagus is "heartburn," a burning pain felt substernally and fairly well localized over the site of stimulation. This pain

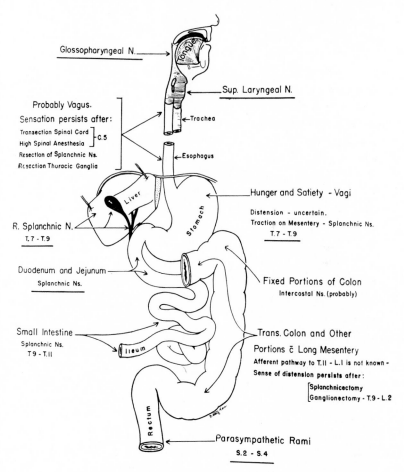

Fig. 18. Afferent nerve pathways for alimentary tract (J. C. White).[29]

has been shown by Jones [63] to be due to spasm of the cardiac end of the esophagus. The spasm may be induced by mechanical, thermal, chemical or electrical stimuli. The commonest cause of heartburn in man is the regurgitation of highly acid gastric juice into the esophagus which has already had its pain threshold lowered by the presence of engorgment or inflammation.

Not only is the pain of heartburn of a burning character but the pain of peptic ulcer which arises from the stomach or duodenum is frequently described as burning. It is of special interest that burning pain, ordinarily associated with noxious stimulation of the skin, can be elicted from the upper gastrointestinal tract and from other mucous membranes as, for example, in the nose.

Stomach and Adjacent Structures: The pathways for afferent impulses from the stomach have not been clearly delineated but those which mediate pain appear to be carried in the splanchnic sympathetic trunks and enter the cord in the seventh to ninth thoracic segments (*See* Figure 18).

The sensibility of the stomach has been explored in a subject with a large gastric stoma.[64] When the mucosa in its normal state was pinched between the blades of a forceps no pain resulted. Likewise the application of 50 and 95 per cent alcohol, 1.0N HCl and 0.1N NaOH and 1:30 suspension of mustard failed to induce pain in the healthy mucosa. When the mucosa was inflamed, however, congested and oedematous from whatever cause, local mechanical and chemical stimulation evoked pain of considerable intensity. Thus, although the number of nerve fibers and endings subserving pain may be relatively small, it has been conclusively shown, by virtue of the fact that pain occurred upon noxious stimulation of the inflamed gastric mucosa, that true visceral pain exists.

These observations have since been confirmed on the mucosae of the bladder [66] and large bowel.[65]

Not only do gastric pains arise from the mucosa but also from deeper structures in the stomach as well. There is considerable evidence to suggest that the muscular layers may be capable of initiating noxious impulses. In experiments on the fistulous subject already referred to it was found that contractions of the stomach in its normal state of a magnitude of 30 millimeters of mercury pressure against an indwelling balloon induced pain. When the stomach was engorged and hyperemic, however, contractions of only 20 millimeters of mercury pressure induced pain.

This pain could hardly come from stretching of mesenteric attachments since there is less traction as the result of 20 millimeters of mercury pressure than of 30 millimeters. It seems likely, therefore, that some of the pain emanates from the structures deeper than the mucosa, namely from the muscularis, the serosa, or the visceral peritoneum. When the stomach was stretched by glass rods it was found that when the contractile state of the stomach was average the pressure necessary to produce pain was 100 gm. per sq. cm. However, when the stomach wall was strongly contracted pressure of fifty gm. per sq. cm. or half that originally applied was found sufficient to produce pain. On the other hand, when the stomach was relatively relaxed, 150 gm. per sq. cm. were necessary to induce pain. These observations suggest that either the muscularis or serosa may contribute to pain experienced from the stomach.

To supplement these experiments on the exposed stomach, indirect but significant evidence comes from the observations of Palmer [136] who has shown that pain from peptic ulcer occurs only when gastric content is acid. It is reduced in intensity or eliminated by emptying the stomach as by emesis or aspiration, and by neutralizing the acid content with food or alkali. Also, in the patient with peptic ulcer, who is temporarily free of pain, injections of dilute hydrochloric acid (0.25, 0.5 and 1.0 per cent) will induce pain. Pain is not induced by the injection of such HCl into the normal stomach, or into stomachs with healed peptic ulcers.

In contrast to those of Palmer,[136] the findings of Ruffin and associates appear to implicate contractile activity in the duodenum as a mechanism for the pain of peptic ulcer.[160] Perhaps it will be found that in the stomach, as elsewhere, an adequate stimulus, be it chemical or mechanical, delivered to pain nerve endings may induce pain. As already pointed out it is generally true that hyperaemia and tissue engorgement serve to lower pain threshold. Indeed the typical "ulcer pattern" of pain-food-relief has been observed frequently in association with gastric hyperfunction but without any detectable evidence of ulcer.

Noxious impulses from the pancreas, liver and biliary tracts appear to travel in the same pathways as do those from the stomach. These facts explain in part the difficulties encountered in differential diagnosis of epigastric pain. Not only may it arise from these structures named but also from retroperitoneal tissues, skeletal muscles or from lesions of the nervous system such as herpes zoster or cord tumors which involve dorsal roots. Epigastric pains may even be referred from the heart or other thoracic structures as mentioned above or from impulses arising in the lower bowel including the transverse colon and appendix. The hepatic parenchyma has not been shown to be pain sensitive but noxious stimulation by rapid distention of its capsule does give rise to pain. The capsule is apparently able to accommodate to very slow distention without the occurrence of pain. The same generalizations apply to other solid organs including the spleen and possibly the kidneys. Pain from the gall bladder has been found to be commonly localized in the distribution of T9 [29] either anteriorly beneath the right costal margin or posteriorly at the angle of scapula.

Small and Large Intestines: Noxious impulses from the small intestine also travel in splanchnic pathways but enter the cord slightly lower from T9 to T11. The afferent innervation of the colon above the sigmoid is also carried in the sympathetic trunks.[137] Below this level it is probably mainly supplied by afferent fibers through its mesenteries from the lower thoracic and upper lumbar segmental nerves without involvement of sympathetic or parasympathetic pathways.[138] The rectum, however, does receive afferent nerves through the parasympathetic rami from S2-S4. (*See* Figure 18.)

Urinary Tract Pain. In the urogenital tract, renal and ureteral pain arises from noxious impulses reaching the cord via the lower splanchnic trunks and the lower two thoracic and first lumbar segments. McClellan and Goodell [25] have shown that ureteral colic often gives rise to secondary painful spasms of lumbo-dorsal muscles which may long outlast the period of noxious stimulation of the ureter or renal pelvis (Figure 10). Painful distention of the detrusor muscles initiates noxious impulses which, like those from the lower colon and rectum appear to travel in segmental nerves in the peritoneum.

From the trigone and structures below the bladder noxious impulses reach the cord over the sacral parasympathetic rami from S2-S4.[29] (*See* Figure 19.) Noxious stimulation of the bladder trigone and region of the urethral origin causes pain to be felt at the distal tip of the urethra. Prostatic pain may be felt in the perineum or referred to the lower lumbar region where it may be confused with skeletal, muscular, nerve, rectal or renal pain. Pains arising from noxious stimulation of the sper-

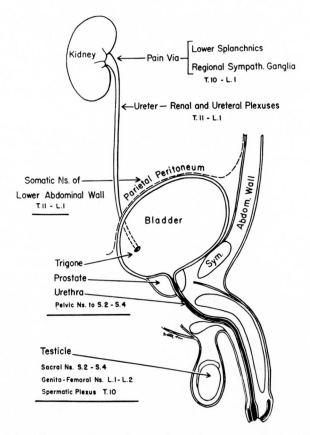

Fig. 19. Afferent nerve pathways for male urogenital tract (J. C. White).[29]

matic cords and testicular structures are felt largely in situ but may be referred up into the hypogastric region where they may be mistaken for colonic or other pains in that region. Down into the testes and along the groin and inner aspects of the thighs the pains of renal colic are commonly referred where they may appear to arise from the spermatic channels or from local vascular lesions such as thrombo-phlebitis.

In the female, noxious impulses arising in the fundus uteri reach the central nervous system by way of the superior hypogastric plexus entering the cord from T10 to L1.[28, 138, 139] From the cervix, on the other hand they travel in the second and fourth sacral nerves with impulses from the bladder neck.[140, 141] Noxious impulses from fallopian tubes and ovaries reach the cord at the tenth thoracic level travelling in the plexus of nerves which accompany the ovarian vessels. Closely contiguous structures including the broad ligaments, other mesenteries and retroperitoneal structures are innervated by branches of the lumbosacral plexus and segmental nerves (*See* Figure 20). Thus to relieve the pain of ovarian carcinoma it is necessary to sever a wide extent of pathways in order to denervate structures almost invariably invaded by the growth.

The commonest pains arising from the female genital structures are the pains of dysmenorrhoea and labor. It is likely that most dysmenorrhoeic pains are related to the subject's reaction to contractions of the uterine musculature. Others may occur, however, from traction on adherent structures, involved in an inflammatory, fibrotic or neoplastic process. The pains of labor doubtless arise from the muscular activity of the fundus uteri.

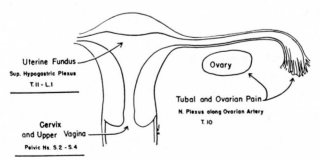

Fig. 20. Afferent nerve pathways for female genital structures (J. C. White).[29]

Chapter III

THE DIAGNOSIS AND MANAGEMENT OF PAINFUL CONDITIONS

An understanding of the nature of pain and the mechanism responsible for its mediation is useful in diagnosis and helpful in differentiating pains from various sources. The history must be taken from the patient with special attention to points which would allow application of data that are known. The most useful description of the pain is likely to be available while the patient is actually experiencing the sensation. Hence, if the original history was obtained during a painless interval, it is profitable to ask the patient to recapitulate his experience while the pain is going on. The following are the most pertinent questions:

1. **Locality.** The site of pain must first be reliably determined together with its extent and whether or not there are secondary areas of reference. Sharply circumscribed pain is characteristic of peptic ulcer for example, while colonic pain is likely to be more diffusely spread over the abdomen.

2. **Quality.** Whether the noxious impulses originate in the superficial or deep structures may often be determined from the quality of the pain. The patients own words are useful in conveying information regarding the significance of the pain and in indicating the degree and nature of his reaction to the experience but quality should be expressed in standard terms, which are known to relate distinguishable aspects of pain. Thus bright, pricking,

burning or itching pains come from the skin while dull aching pains characteristically arise in deeper structures. Burning pain is also known to arise from the mucus membrane of the nose and upper gastrointestinal tract.

3. Temporal Factors. It is important to know whether the pain is intermittent, continuous, pulsatile, or characterized by wave-like rise and fall in intensity. Knowledge of the length of duration of a painful experience is also essential. The pain of migraine, for example is characteristically pulsatile and lasts all day while the pains of tic douloureux are intermittent, individual tics occurring in volleys for seconds, and attacks last for a few minutes to an hour or two. The length of the interval between painful episodes may also serve to distinguish the structure involved. The occurrence of pain from noxious stimulation in the upper gastro-intestinal tract is likely to bear some relation to meals while that from the lowermost portion is more apt to be related temporally to defecation. Painful joints usually hurt most in cold, damp weather. Other pains are related to special times of the day or seasons of the year.

4. Circumstances Under Which Pain Occurs or is Aggravated. Pleuritic pain is ordinarily associated with breathing, heart muscle pain with exercise, peptic ulcer pain with an acid containing stomach empty of food, and rectal pain with urgency to defecate. The pain from lesions involving spinal roots are likely to be accentuated by coughing, straining or sneezing while the headache following lumbar puncture is regularly accentuated when the patient assumes the upright posture. Most pains may be noted to occur or be aggravated under certain specific circumstances and this characteristic is often highly useful in diagnosis.

5. Factors Which Reduce Pain. Digital pressure over the carotid or temporal arteries is likely to afford transitory relief from migraine headache; locally applied heat often reduces the intensity of pain from muscle tension. Analgesics reduce the intensity of pains in general. Knowledge of whether or not a given pain can be obliterated by the threshold raising effects of a certain analgesic provides the physician with a rough index of its intensity.

6. Intensity. Intensity is likely to be the most difficult aspect of the pain for a patient to describe and for the physician to recognize. This may be partly due to confusion in the minds of both regarding the distinction between pain perception and reaction. Since it is known to be possible to distinguish and recall, with reasonable accuracy, various grades of pain intensity, it is useful to ask the patient to compare in terms of plusses his own estimate of intensity using 10 plus for the most intense pain he has ever experienced. Another method whereby the intensity of a patient's pain may be roughly calibrated by the physician is as follows: He first pinches with moderate force his patient's biceps indicating that such a pain is of approximately 2 plus intensity. A pinch of roughly twice that force is then administered and designated as 4 plus. Finally, an extremely forceful pinch is administered and designated as 8 plus. The patient is then asked to evaluate the intensity of his own pain in terms of these standards.

7. Associated Phenomena. There are certain identifying bodily changes which may regularly accompany certain varieties of painful conditions. Such disturbances would include unilateral lachrymation and swelling of the eyelids occasionally accompanying migraine, spasm and flushing of the face during an attack of tic douloureux, muscular movements both localized and generalized, protective gestures and positions assumed during pain.

8. Examination. In the examination of the patient special features to be noted are the presence or absence of local, deep tenderness or surface hyperalgesia, other sensory and motor phenomena, vascular disturbances, changes in sweating and skin temperature and muscle spasm. When pain is in the chest, a friction rub or alteration of the heart sounds may establish the origin of pain. When pain is in the abdomen it is equally important to listen for borborygmi and palpate for organs. In general, a careful analysis of a patient's painful experience by well-directed questioning and examining for relevant features greatly increases the likelihood of accurate diagnosis.

Therapy Directed at Peripheral Pain Mechanisms. In the treatment of painful conditions it is sometimes possible to interrupt or eradicate the peripheral mechanism responsible for pain. Most of the common mechanisms have already been mentioned, they include 1) distention and displacement of pain-sensitive vascular structures; 2) sustained contraction of skeletal muscles; 3) relative ischemia of various structures, especially striated muscles; 4) unusually vigorous contraction of or distention of muscle structures, especially parts of the digestive and genitourinary tubes; 5) pulling, pinching or displacement of connective tissues structures, including periosteum and dura; and 6) inflammatory reactions involving serous membranes and other structures.

Among the commonest painful conditions with which the physician has to contend are headaches, due to painful distention of cranial arteries. These mechanisms are discussed in detail on page 48. Clinically, vascular headaches may be recognized by their pulsatile quality and by the fact that pain may be temporarily interrupted by digital compression of an arterial trunk supplying the painful area, for example, branches of the temporal or carotid artery on one side. During the course of a vascular headache pain may be aborted by the administration of an effective vasoconstrictor agent. Such an agent is ergotamine tartrate. It can be administered intramuscularly in 1 mg. dosage, or half that amount may be given intravenously. Intravenous administration should not be undertaken unless there is previous evidence from intramuscular dosage that the patient tolerates the drug well. Injections of ergotamine should not be given more frequently than once a week and not at all during pregnancy or in the presence of hypertension or cardiac decompensation.

Like the arteries other muscular tubes such as the gut, biliary tract and ureters are pain sensitive to stimuli which distend or distort them. Spasms of tubular structures in the gastrointestinal and urinary tracts also appear to be capable of inducing pain by virtue of the stretching effects of the dilatation behind the construction. Reduction of pain intensity may be secured by agents whose antispasmodic action is powerful enough to overcome the forces which induce spasm. Atropine sulfate 0.0012 gm. administered hypodermically or 0.0018 gm. by mouth will provide nearly maximal effect without incapacitating side effects. Anticholinergic agents, e.g., Banthine* in well tolerated doses of 50-150 mg. may be more effective. This agent may be given at four to six hour intervals around the clock.

Another commonly encountered pain is that which is attributable to ischemia of striated muscle. The pain of angina pectoris appears to fall in this category as well as the pain of Raynaud's syndrome and intermittent claudication. Pain may be abolished by vasodilator drugs such as glyceryl trinitrate, by other maneuvers which increase local circulation, or by placing the muscles at rest and thus reducing their metabolic demands. Nonmuscular structures such as the brain, lungs, kidneys and liver do not evoke pain during ischemia. Pain in these structures

---

* G. D. Searle & Co. brand of methantheline bromide.

occurs when their membranous envelopes or attachments are stretched or inflamed. Treatment of such inflammatory reactions is, of course, directed at the causal factor if it is known. Under such circumstances the pains often yield to appropriate antibiotic agents. The pain of more obscure inflammatory reactions such as rheumatoid arthritis may be reduced or abolished by cortisone or ACTH.

It seems likely that the pains which are most frequently encountered in clinical practice occur in part because of unduly sustained increase in the contractile state of skeletal muscle. The pain of a broken arm or leg, for example, is due in part to sustained contraction of muscles attempting to splint the fragments. The pain of poliomyelitis may also include such a mechanism. A host of headaches, stiff necks and pains in the back and extremities depend upon the same mechanism. The underlying physiology has not been altogether elucidated as indicated earlier in this volume, but it is empirically true that reduction of pain intensity may be accomplished by means which relax muscles or increase the circulation locally. Thus sedatives, especially intravenously administered sodium amytal 0.2 gm. —0.5 gm. in 10 per cent solution are effective. This agent should be injected slowly at the rate of not more than 1 cc./min. Pain from contracted muscles will yield to injections of curare, but these are too hazardous and their effects too transitory to make them of practical clinical value. Mephensesin* administered intravenously in 2 per cent solution, 100 cc. over four or five minutes has similar effects but is less dangerous than curare. Its transitory action, however, makes it of little use in therapy, although it may be helpful diagnostically. There is little evidence that the agent is specifically effective when taken by mouth. Local heat from

---

* Called Myonesin in British publications and known by various trade names in the U.S.A., such as Tolserol (E. R. Squibb & Co.).

moist towels or a hot tub is helpful and if the difficulty is reasonably well localized and persistent, it may yield to infiltrations of 1 per cent or 2 per cent procaine locally. This agent may both relax the muscles responsible for the pain by blocking efferent nerve impulses or interrupt impulses from noxious stimuli carried in the afferent nerves so that pain is not felt. Often when the painful process is adequately interrupted it will not recur. When it does, repeated injection of procaine locally may ultimately be followed by disappearance of the pain.

Physicians faced with the myriad aches and pains encountered in medical practice do well to analyze as precisely as possible the mechanism which underlies the troublesome sensations. Usually it will fit into one of the six categories named. Therapeutically it is more important to deal with a patient's reaction to pain than with his perception since it is suffering that brings the patient to the physician. In the case of headaches and other painful states it has been shown that certain individuals overreact to minor disturbances at the end organ and thus may become incapacitated by a painful sensation which another individual might ignore.[142] Pain-relieving drugs which interrupt the peripheral mechanisms responsible for pain must be distinguished from analgesics which modify sensory perception or reaction. Examples of the former group are atropine which may relieve the pain of smooth muscle spasm by relieving the spasm, and ergotamine which interrupts the mechanism for migraine headache by constricting over-distended arteries.[45] Neither of these drugs are, strictly speaking, analgesics.

ANALGESIC AGENTS

Among analgesics several drugs have been tested for their effect on pain threshold in man. Some, such as acetylsalicylic acid, acetanilid, acetophenetidin and aminopyrine, act primarily on the threshold for pain perception although there is also a significant effect upon the reaction to pain.[58] In the case of each agent an optimal dosage was found which afforded close to maximum pain-relieving action. Increasing the amount administered beyond this point did not further raise pain threshold significantly, prolonged the effect only slightly and accentuated undesirable side-effects.[51]

It has been shown that there is a quantitative relationship between the effects of analgesic agents on the pain threshold and upon the intensity of the pain experienced. The various analgesic agents were found to reduce the intensity of either deep or superficial pain in a fashion comparable to their threshold raising effects.[82]

It was found that the combination of two analgesic agents did not produce an additive effect but merely the effect of the stronger agent. Repeated administration of one agent so as to keep the threshold high was found the most effective way of dealing with pain as far as perception is concerned.

The more potent analgesics including opiates and alcohol, owe their efficacy primarily to their ability to control reaction to pain although they are capable of raising the threshold for perception of pain as well.[57, 58] It has been shown that the relaxation, apathy and freedom from anxiety which follows the administration of morphine long outlasts its effects on the threshold for pain perception.

As mentioned earlier, it has long been observed that the presence of pain elevates the threshold for perception of another pain. The presence of pain also modifies the action of analgesics, reducing materially their pain threshold raising properties. The pain threshold raising capacity of morphine for example, is almost obliterated when a noxious stimulus is introduced immediately before its injection. Less effect was noted when pain was induced at various intervals after the administration of morphine. This effect has been described by Cushny [143] who observed, in patients with constant pains which were alleviated by morphine, that a suddenly introduced new noxious stimulus seemed to be acutely appreciated as if the patient had had no morphine.

The presence of pain was also found to reduce the psychological effects of morphine. This action was especially noticeable when a sustained painful stimulus was withdrawn from a subject who had received morphine. The withdrawal of pain was followed by a feeling of apathy and lethargy similar to that which would be experienced from a fresh injection of morphine. This effect may explain why addiction to morphine appears to be less readily acquired by individuals suffering from sustained intensely painful conditions.

Morphine Substitutes. Numerous synthetic drugs have been developed as morphine substitutes with the hope of: 1) effecting a higher elevation of pain threshold or a greater reduction in pain sensibility, and 2) avoiding the habit forming qualities of morphine. Thus far these efforts have not been successful chiefly because, in pain of maximal intensity in which a 75 per cent reduction of perception is the most that can be hoped for with the agents available their effect on reaction to pain becomes more and more relied upon. Since it appears that addiction to an agent stems largely from its ability to reduce anxiety and induce a state of relative detachment, it is unlikely that any analgesic will be developed which will assuage the distress of pain without also alleviating the torments from the "slings and arrows of outrageous fortune." To the extent to which it would do this, the agent would be a potential habit former.

As shown by the studies of Beecher [9] and later by

Papper and associates [144] and Dodson and Bennett [145] only a few patients experience high intensity pain during the early post-operative period although anxiety and reactivity to pain may be at a high pitch. This is a period when narcotics and sedatives are likely to be given too freely, but it is also a period in which the undesirable side effects of narcotics and sedatives are most dangerous and most definitely militate against a smooth post-operative recovery. Dodson and his associates [145] found that they were able to keep their patients relatively free of suffering by ready availability of attention from the nurses and sterile saline hypodermics whenever relief of pain was requested. It was judged that these patients were made as comfortable during the early post-operative period as those who received opiates frequently and at regular intervals. On the second and third day postoperatively the placebo patients did vastly better with fewer gas pains, early spontaneous bowel movements and better appetite.

Although there should probably be more proscription than prescription of narcotics and sedatives on the first two days following surgical operations, it is, of course, not possible to eliminate them altogether. They should not be used routinely, however. Each patient should be evaluated as carefully as possible from the standpoint of pain intensity and given reassurance.

SURGICAL MEASURES FOR THE RELIEF OF PAIN

When pain is intractable to other measures there remain four principal ways in which it may be reduced or abolished by surgery: 1) By extirpation of the painful part, as for example, in the case of removal of a peptic ulcer. 2) Interruption of peripheral afferent fibers by alcohol injection or section or peripheral nerves or sympathetic trunks. 3) By section of sensory nerve roots. 4) By section of tracts within the central nervous system.

Section of posterior spinal roots is a valuable procedure when the afferent inflow is clearly defined and limited to a small number of spinal segments.[146] It has proven of most value in cases with localized pain in the neck and trunk. In the treatment of pain in the upper extremity it is perhaps less satisfactory, but here, too, it has certain value which is best illustrated in the beneficial results of root section in patients with pain from neoplasms at the apex of the chest.[146]

Heart pain from coronary insufficiency, when intractable, may be effectively treated by resection of the upper four or five thoracic sympathetic ganglia bilaterally. The procedure not only interrupts cardioaccelerator and vasomotor fibers which may be concerned with the mechanism of some anginal pains, but it cuts off all or most of the afferent pain nerves from the heart.[147]

Pain from most abdominal viscera can be abolished by removal of parts or all of the sympathetic chain which carries the afferent fibers. In the midline structures such as the stomach, pancreas, and small intestine, it is necessary to perform the sympathectomy bilaterally, however, in order to de-afferent the structure and eliminate pain.[148, 149]

When the exact segmental inflow from a painful area is uncertain or spread over a large number of spinal roots, chordotomy gives consistent and satisfactory relief of pain when it is possible to section, selectively the spinothalamic tract.[106] In subjects with intractable pain about the head and neck, medullary tractotomy has been successfully performed.[150]

The neurosurgical measures for the elimination of pain have been carefully reviewed by White and Sweet.[4] They analyze the reports in the literature as well as their own surgical experience in attempting to relieve somatic and visceral pain at various levels. They particularly emphasize the value of section of the spino-thalamic tract if the technic is precise enough and if certain rules are observed. They point to the importance of careful psychiatric screening of patients to eliminate those who are severely psychoneurotic or addicted to narcotics. According to these authors it is especially important to check the extent of anesthesia before completing the operation. They find the procedure of tractotomy relatively safe up to the level of the mid brain. With even the most gratifying elimination of pain by a neurosurgical procedure, however, there is always some risk of decrease in the size of the anesthetic area and recurrence of pain.

Notable among painful situations in which neurosurgical procedures on the peripheral nerves, roots, cord or brain stem have not been helpful is the so-called central pain of the thalamic syndrome or in causalgia or phantom limb. Similarly such surgical procedures have not been of reliable help in treating post-herpetic neuritis or the ill defined conditions grouped together as atypical facial neuralgia. Even lobotomy has provided only limited and inconsistent relief to patients suffering from these various obscure conditions.

The evidence of several investigators [151, 152, 153] suggests that many of the effects of lobotomy result from isolating portions of the cortex from the activating systems. Some degree of cerebral organization is lost after the various modifications of the lobotomy procedure. The deficit appears to be related more to the quantity of cortical tissue destroyed rather than to the precise locality of the destruction.[154]

Surgical procedures on the cerebral cortex, like narcotic drugs, have been found to affect pain reaction profoundly.[155, 156, 157, 158] It is therefore likely that relief of pain by cortical surgery derives mainly from cutting off or inactivating circuits concerned with the significance of the experience thereby mitigating the anguish of pain. For example, after bilateral lobotomy for pain from a "phantom limb" perception of the pain persisted but the subject was no longer troubled by the pain and mentioned it only when questioned.

Lobotomized subjects upon whom quantitative testing procedures have been done display no elevation of pain threshold or impairment of pain perception at threshold level, although their ability to discriminate differences in pain intensity above threshold level and their reactivity to pain may be greatly altered.[159] Moreover it has been observed following lobotomy for intractable pain in subjects who have become addicted to morphine that the craving for the drug is often remarkably inconspicuous following operation.

In general it should be said that the success of neurosurgical procedures for the elimination of pain is very closely related not only to the adequacy of the surgeon's knowledge of the source and mechanism of the pain but also his knowledge of the patient's temperment and past life adjustment. Patients who are unduly "body conscious" and whose suffering is largely a matter of over-reaction to low intensity stimuli are likely to fix their preoccupation on the post-operative state and may actually be made more miserable by surgery. Similarly those who may have been relatively well adjusted may lose morale and be greatly worsened by unsuccessful surgical intervention.

WHEN THE PROGNOSIS IS POOR

It is well known that the equanimity of a strong physician rubs off to some extent on his patient. In line with the wise words of Oliver Wendell Holmes, "It is the physician's privilege to cure seldom, to relieve often, and to comfort always." The good physician is never in a position to say to his patient, "There is nothing more I can do for you." There is always something that can be done by way of relieving the suffering of the patient. The physician's innate compassion and liking for his fellow man becomes at this point a most powerful therapeutic weapon, one with which to begin and one with which to end at the bedside of the dying.

Often the physician loses important opportunities to help his patient by failing adequately to communicate with him. His own psychological defenses may obscure his view of the patient's needs and may lead to brusque attitudes on the one hand or excessive levity on the other prompting such remarks as, "I'll see you on the golf course in a few weeks." Making light of the situation so that it is impossible for the patient to talk to the doctor, to approach him, is perhaps the commonest way in which the physician protects himself against anxiety in this very important communication with the patient.

The generally increased awareness of the importance of a good psychological adjustment in illness has often led to referral to the psychiatrist of patients who are difficult to handle or who have prominent emotional needs. While help from a psychiatrist may occasionally be indicated and even crucial, the realistic solution of the problem requires that the physician assume a direct and participating interest.

THE CARE OF THE DYING

At the bedside of the dying there is another important opportunity for individualized judgments. Some patients want to know how sick they are. Others prefer the information to be withheld. Some patients prefer to die alone, others with their families about them. Some would prefer to be so narcotized as to be unaware of their fading life while others prefer the awareness of life as long as it lasts. The decision as to how to handle the situation is therefore made on the basis of the physician's knowledge of his patient's personality. He must enlist the cooperation of the nurses and other ward personnel to follow a consistent plan which will provide the greatest comfort for his patient. The comfort of the dying is rarely contributed to by an atmosphere of hectic application of heroic last minute, would-be life saving measures such as transfusions and infusions and other needle therapy, oxygen tents and pulmotors. On the other hand it may be discouraging to a patient for the physician suddenly to clear the room of such devices in anticipation of death. The most important thing is for the physician to communicate with his patient so that he can help him with what he wants and needs most during his last hours. It is rarely necessary to talk much but it is extremely important to listen and to be aware of communications other than verbal ones. The strength and ability of the patient to meet this phase of life—because, after all, death is an aspect of life—depend on a great many things that strengthen his courage and faith. The doctor is a dominant figure in the patient's ebbing life. Therefore rather than keeping the patient at arms length, rather than making light, rather than deceiving himself that the patient is so extraordinarily stoical, the physician should attempt to share his patient's experience in a dignified and steadfast way.

There is always the urge to "do something" and frequently this inward urge of the physician is strongly reinforced by demands of the patient's family. The one important thing to do is to see the patient frequently, to provide him often with the reassuring presence of the doctors and nurses and other members of the staff. It is also important for the doctor to speak frequently with the family, if only to tell them that there is no change, and to be available to answer their anxious questions. The key to equanimity of the dying and of the family is the early establishment of an interested, sympathetic relationship giving the patient the assurance that the physician is doing his utmost and will support his patient to the last.

GENERAL PRINCIPLES IN THE MANAGEMENT OF PAIN AND THE SUFFERING PATIENT

In the management of painful conditions, then, it is important to recognize the function of pain as an indicator of disease. The presence of pain in any part usually calls for an investigation of its underlying cause rather than merely the relief of the patient. In the case of abdominal pain, for example, the pain itself is such an important diagnostic guide that it is hazardous to administer analgesics before its cause is reliably determined.

The most rational therapy for pain involves, not the use of analgesics or mutilating surgical procedures, but the interruption of the mechanism which produces pain. Analgesics are administered only when the latter cannot be satisfactorily accomplished. For the proper choice of analgesics it is important to obtain, if possible, some estimate of how long the painful condition is likely to persist. Addiction to morphine has frequently followed its prolonged use for the relief of chronic pains. The hazard of addiction is always present but often the need for narcotics may be reduced by attention to details of the patient's comfort, pillow supports in painful areas, skin care, etc. The newer "tranquilizing" drugs may have value as adjuncts to analgesic and sedative therapy for pain but definitive data on their applicability are still lacking. Alcohol is a reasonably potent analgesic with fewer undesirable side effects than opiates.

It is important to estimate, if possible, how much of the patient's discomfort is due to the perception of pain from noxious stimuli and how much may represent over-reaction to minor disturbances at the end-organ. Complaints of the latter type are common and are often treated more appropriately with reassurance and emotional support from the physician and attention to the individual's personality and life situation than with analgesic drugs or other palliative measures.

REFERENCES

1. KEELE, C. A.: *Anatomies of Pain.* Springfield, Thomas, 1957.

2. HARDY, J. D., WOLFF, H. G., and GOODELL, H.: *Pain Sensations and Reactions.* Baltimore, Williams & Wilkins, 1952.

3. BONICA, J. J.: *The Management of Pain.* Philadelphia, Lea, 1953.

4. WHITE, JAMES C., and SWEET, WILLIAM H.: *Pain: Its Mechanism and Neurosurgical Control.* Springfield, Thomas, 1953.

5. FORD, FRANK R., and WILKINS, LAWSON: Congenital universal insensitiveness to pain. *Bull. Johns Hopkins Hosp.*, 62:448, 1938.

6. KUNKLE, E. CHARLES, and CHAPMAN, WILLIAM P.: Insensitivity to pain in man. *Proc. A. Res. Nerv. & Ment. Dis.*, 23:100, 1943.

7. WEST, LOUIS J.: Data to be published.

8. PAVLOV, I. P.: *Conditioned Reflexes.* London, Oxford, 1927.

9. BEECHER, HENRY K.: Pain in men wounded in battle. *Ann. Surg.*, 123:96, 1946.

10. GOLD, H., KWIT, N. T., and MODELL, W.: The effect of extracardiac pain on the heart. *Proc. A. Res. Nerv. & Ment. Dis.*, 23:345, 1943.

11. WOLF, GEORGE: The effect of pain on renal function. *Proc. A. Res. Nerv. & Ment. Dis.*, 23:358, 1943.

12. HOLMES, T. H., GOODELL, H., WOLF, S., and WOLFF, H. G.: Changes in the nasal function associated with variations in emotional state and life situation. *Tr. Am. Acad. Ophth.*, 51:449, 1947.

13. WOLF, STEWART, and ALMY, THOMAS, P.: Experimental observations on cardiospasm in man. *Gastroenterology, 13*:401, 1949.

14. WOLF, STEWART, and WOLFF, H. G.: *Human Gastric Function. An Experimental Study of a Man and His Stomach.* 2nd ed. New York, Oxford, 1947.

15. DUNCAN, C. H., STEVENSON, I., and RIPLEY, H. S.: Life situations, emotions and paroxysmal auricular arrhythmias. *Psychosom. Med., 12*:23, 1950.

16. WOLF, S., PFEIFFER, J. B., RIPLEY, H. S., WINTER, O. S., and WOLFF, H. G.: Hypertension as a reaction pattern to stress; summary of experimental data on variations in blood pressure and renal blood flow. *Ann. Int. Med., 29*:1056, 1948.

17. WOLF, STEWART, and HARDY, JAMES D.: Studies on pain: Observations on pain due to local cooling and on factors involved in the "cold pressor" effect. *J. Clin. Investigation, 20*:521, 1941.

18. GASSER, HERBERT S.: Conduction in nerves in relation to fiber types. *Proc. A. Res. Nerv. & Ment. Dis., 23*: 44, 1943.

19. CLARK, D., HUGHES, J., and GASSER, H. S.: Afferent function in the group of nerve fibers of slowest conduction velocity. *Am. J. Physiol., 114*:69, 1935.

20. GASSER, HERBERT S., and ERLANGER, J.: The role of fiber size in the establishment of a nerve block by pressure or cocaine. *Am. J. Physiol., 88*:581, 1929.

21. TOWER, SARAH S.: Pain. Definition and properties of the unit for sensory reception. *Proc. A. Res. Nerv. & Ment. Dis., 23*:16, 1943.

22. WOOLLARD, H. H., WEDDELL, G., and HARPMAN, J. A.: Observations on the neurohistological basis of cutaneous pain. *J. Anat., 74*:413, 1940.

23. WEDDELL, GRAHAM: The pattern of cutaneous innervation in relation to cutaneous sensibility. *J. Anat., 75*: 346, 1941.

24. WEDDELL, GRAHAM: The multiple innervation of sensory spots in the skin. *J. Anat., 75:*441, 1941.

25. GASSER, HERBERT S.: Pain-producing impulses in peripheral nerves. *Proc. A. Res. Nerv. & Ment. Dis., 23:* 44, 1943.

26. FÖRSTER, O.: *Die Leitungsbahnen des Schmerzgefuhls und die Chirurgieche Behandlung der Schmerzzustande.* Berlin, Urban, 1927.

27. JONNESCO, T., and ENARCHESO, M.: Experimentalle Untersuchungen über die afferenten Kardie aortalen Bahnen und uber den physiologischen Nachweis der Existenz des Depresser als isolierter Nerv beim Menschen. *Ztschr. f. d. ges. esper. Med., 48:*490 and 516, 1926.

28. LERICHE, R., and FONTAINE, R.: Chirugie des Nerfs du coeur. *P. Verb. Congr. Fr. Chir., 41:*89, 1932.

29. WHITE, JAMES C.: Sensory innervation of the viscera: studies on visceral afferent neurons in man based on neurosurgical procedures for relief of intractable pain. *Proc. A. Res. Nerv. & Ment. Dis., 23:*373, 1943.

30. LANGLEY, J. N.: Trophic center of afferent sympathetic fibers. *J. Physiol., 16:*33, 1905-6.

31. ERLANGER, JOSEPH, and GASSER, HERBERT, S.: *Electrical Signs of Nervous Activity.* Philadelphia, Univ. Penn. Press, 1937.

32. GORDON, G., and WHITTERIDGE, D.: Conduction time for human pain sensation. *Lancet, 2:*700, 1943.

33. BIGELOW, N., HARRISON, I., GOODELL, H., and WOLFF, H. G.: Studies on Pain: Quantitative measurements of two pain sensations of the skin, with reference to the nature of the "hyperalgesia of peripheral neuritis." *J. Clin. Investigation, 23:*503, 1945.

34. LEWIS, THOMAS: *Pain.* New York, MacMillan, 1942.

35. FÖRSTER, O., and GAGEL, O.: Die Verderseitenstrangdurchsschneidung bein Menschen. *Ztschr. f. d. ges. Neurol., 138:*1, 1932.

36. Spiller, W. G., and Martin, Edward: The treatment of persistent pain of organic origin in the lower part of the body by division of the anterolateral column of the spinal cord. *J.A.M.A.*, *68*:1489, 1912.

37. Stopford, John S. B.: *Sensation and the Sensory Pathway.* London, Longmans, 1930.

38. French, Lyle A., and Peyton, William T.: Ipsilateral sensory loss following cordotomy. *J. Neurosurg.*, *5:* 403, 1948.

39. Voris, Harold C.: Ipsilateral sensory loss following chordotomy: Report of a case. *Arch. Neurol. & Psychiat.*, *65*:95, 1951.

40. Walker, A. Earl: Central representation of pain. *Proc. A. Res. Nerv. & Ment. Dis.*, *23*:63, 1943.

41. Sweet, W. H., Selverstone, B., and Nilges, R.: Sensory responses from anterior roots and from surface and interior of spinal cord in man. *Tr. Am. Neurol. A.*, *75:* 165, 1950.

42. Hardy, J. D., Wolff, H. G., and Goodell, H.: The effect of skin temperature upon the pain threshold evoked by thermal radiation. *Science, 114*:49, 1951.

43. Ostfeld, A. M., Chapman, L. F., Goodell, H., and Wolff, H. G.: Studies on headache; summary of evidence concerning a noxious agent active locally during migraine headache. *Psychosom. Med.*, *19*:199, 1957.

44. Beecher, Henry K.: Relationship of significance of wound to pain experienced. *J.A.M.A.*, *161*:1609. 1956.

45. Graham, J. R., and Wolff, Harold G.: Mechanism of migraine headache and action of ergotamine tartrate. *Proc. A. Res. Nerv. & Ment. Dis.*, *18*:638, 1937.

46. Ray, Bronson, S., and Wolff, Harold G.: Experiment studies on headache. Pain sensitive structures of the head and their significance in headache. *Arch. Surg.*, *41*:813, 1940.

47. Armstrong, D., Jepson, J. B., Keele, C. A., and Stewart, J. W.: Pain-producing substance in human inflammatory exudates and plasma. *J. Physiol.*, *135*:350, 1957.

48. GOETZL, F. R., BURRILL, D. Y., and IVY, A. C.: A critical analysis of algesimetric methods with suggestions for a useful procedure. *Quart. Bull Northwestern Univ. M. School*, 17:280, 1943.

49. CHAPMAN, WILLIAM P., and JONES, C. M.: Variations in cutaneous and visceral pain sensitivity. *J. Clin. Investigation*, 23:81, 1944.

50. HARRISON, IRVING B., and BIGELOW, NOLTON H.: Quantitative studies of visceral pain produced by the contraction of ischemic muscle. *Proc. A. Res. Nerv. & Ment. Dis.*, 23:154, 1943.

51. HARDY, J. D., WOLFF, H. G., and GOODELL, H.: Studies on pain: A new method of measuring pain threshold; observations on spatial summation of pain. *J. Clin Investigation*, 19:649, 1940.

52. HARDY, J. D., WOLFF, H. G., and GOODELL, H.: The pain threshold in man. *Proc. A. Res. Nerv. & Ment. Dis.*, 23:1, 1944.

53. HARDY, J. D., WOLFF, H. G., and GOODELL, H.: Studies on pain: measurements of aching pain threshold and discrimination of differences in intensity of aching pain. *J. Appl. Physiol.*, 5:247, 1952.

54. SCHUMACHER, G. A., GOODELL, H., HARDY, J. D., and WOLFF, H. G.: Uniformity of the pain threshold in man. *Science*, 92:110, 1940.

55. HARDY, J. D., WOLFF, H. G., and GOODELL, H.: Pricking pain threshold in different body areas. *Proc. Soc. Exper. Biol. & Med.*, 80:425, 1952.

56. HUKOVIC, S., and STERN, P.: Transmission of pain perception in the human skin. *Arch. internat. pharmacodyn.*, 109:285, 1957.

57. WOLFF, H. G., HARDY, J. D., and GOODELL, H.: Studies on pain: Measurement of the effect of morphine, codeine, and other opiates on the pain threshold and an analysis of their relation to the pain experience. *J. Clin. Investigation*, 19:659, 1940.

58. WOLFF, H. G., HARDY, J. D., and GOODELL, H.: Measurement of the effect on the pain threshold of acetylsalicylic acid, acetanilid, acetophenetidin, aminopyrine, ethyl alcohol, trichlorethylene, a barbiturate, quinine, ergotamine tartrate and caffeine: an analysis of their relationship to the pain experience. *J. Clin. Investigation,* 20:63, 1941.

59. WOLFF, H. G., and GOODELL, H.: The relation of attitude and suggestion to the perception of and reaction to pain. *Proc. A. Res. Nerv. & Ment. Dis.,* 23:434, 1943.

60. HARDY, J. D., WOLFF, H. G., and GOODELL, H.: Experimental evidence of the nature of cutaneous hyperalgesia. *J. Clin. Investigation,* 29:115, 1950.

61. SCHUMACHER, GEORGE A.: The influence of inflammation on the pain threshold of the skin in man. *Proc. A. Res. Nerv. & Ment. Dis.,* 23:66, 1943.

62. MCAULIFFE, G. W., GOODELL, H., and WOLFF, H. G.: Experimental studies on headache: Pain from the nasal and paranasal structures. *Proc. A. Res. Nerv. & Ment. Dis.,* 23:185, 1943.

63. JONES, CHESTER M.: *Digestive Tract Pain.* Diagnosis and Treatment. Experimental Observations. New York, Macmillan, 1938.

64. WOLF, STEWART, and WOLFF, H. G.: Pain arising from the stomach and mechanisms underlying gastric symptoms. *Proc. A. Res. Nerv. & Ment. Dis.,* 23:289, 1943.

65. ALMY, THOMAS P., and TULIN, M.: Alterations in colonic function in man under stress. Experimental production of changes simulating the irritable colon. *Gastroenterology,* 8:616, 1947.

66. MCLELLAN, ALLISTER M., and GOODELL, HELEN: Pain from the bladder, ureter, and kidney pelvis. *Proc. A. Res. Nerv. & Ment. Dis.,* 23:252, 1943.

67. BILISOLY, F. N., GOODELL, H., and WOLFF, H. G.: Vasodilatation, lowered pain threshold and increased tissue vulnerability. *Arch. Int. Med.,* 94:759, 1954.

68. GRAHAM, D. T., GOODELL, H., and WOLFF, H. G.: Studies on pain: the relation between cutaneous vasodilatation, pain threshold and spontaneous itching and pain. *Am. J. M. Sc., 234:*420, 1957.

69. WOLFF, H. G., HARDY, J. D., and GOODELL, H.: Studies on pain: Measurement of the effect of ethyl alcohol on the pain threshold and on the "alarm" reaction. *J. Pharmacol. & Exper. Therap., 75:*38, 1942.

70. CHAPMAN, W. H., COHEN, M. E., and COBB, S.: Measurement of levels of heat stimulus perceived as painful and producing winces and withdrawal reactions in patients with neurocirculatory asthenia, anxiety neurosis, or effort syndrome and in control subjects. *J. Clin. Investigation, 25:*890, 1946.

71. LIBMAN, E.: Observations on sensitiveness to pain. *Tr. A. Am. Physicians, 41:*305, 1926.

72. HOLLANDER, E.: Clinical gauge for sensitivity to pain. *J. Lab. & Clin. Med., 24:*537, 1939.

73. HINES, EDGAR A., and BROWN, G. E.: A standard stimulus for measuring vasomotor reactions: Its application in the study of hypertension. *Proc. Staff Meet. Mayo Clin., 7:*332, 1932.

74. DALLENBACH, K. M.: Pain: History and present status. *Am. J. Psychol., 52:*331, 1939.

75. ARISTOTLE: *Treatise on the Principles of Life.* (English translation by W. A. Hammond), London, 1902.

76. DARWIN, ERASMUS: *Zoonomia.* London, Johnson, 1794-1796.

77. SCHIFF, M.: Lehrbuch der physiologie, muskel, und nervenphysiologie. *Schavenburg, fahr, 1:*228, 1858.

78. BLIX, MAGNUS: Experimentelle Beitrage zur Losung der Frage uber die specifische Energei der Hautnerven. *Ztschr. f. Biol., 20:*141, 1884.

79. GOLDSCHEIDER, ALFRED: *Gesammelte Abhandlungen.* Leipzig, Barth, 1898.

80. VON FREY, M.: *Die Gefühle und ihr Verhältnis zu den Emfindungen.* Beit. z. Physiol. des Schmersinnes. Berichte über die verhandlung d. königl. sächs. Gesellschaft d. Wissenshaften, Leipzig, 1894.

81. HARDY, J. D., WOLFF, H. G., and GOODELL, H.: Studies on pain: Discrimination of differences in intensity of painful stimuli as a basis of a scale of pain intensity. *J. Clin. Investigation, 26:*1152, 1947.

82. WIKLER, A., GOODELL, H., and WOLFF, H. G.: Studies on pain: The effects of analgesic agents on sensations other than pain. *J. Pharmacol. & Exper. Therap., 83:* 4, 1945.

83. GREENE, L. C., and HARDY, JAMES D.: Spatial summation of pain, abs. *Federation Proc., 16:*50, 1957.

84. *Genuine Works of Hippocrates.* (Translated by Francis Adams.) London, 1859.

85. GAMMON, GEORGE D., and STARR, ISAAC: Studies on the relief of pain by counterirritation. *J. Clin. Investigation, 20:*13, 1941.

86. BERLIN, L., GOODELL, H., and WOLFF, H. G.: Studies on pain: The relation of pain perception and the central inhibitory effect of noxious stimulation to the phenomenon of extinction. *Arch. Neurol. & Psychiat.* In Press.

87. KUNKLE, E. C., KIBLER, R. F., ARMISTEAD, G. C., and GOODELL, H.: Central sensory excitation and inhibition in response to induced pain. *Tr. Am. Neurol. A., 74:* 64, 1949.

88. WOLFF, H. G., and HARDY, J. D.: The nature of pain. *Physiol. Rev.,* 1946.

89. RAY, BRONSON S., and WOLFF, HAROLD G.: Studies on pain: "Spread of pain," evidence on site of spread within the neuraxis of effects of painful stimulation. *Arch. Neurol. & Psychiat., 53:*257, 1945.

90. HARDY, J. D., WOLFF, H. G., and GOODELL, H.: Studies on pain: Observations on the heralgesia associated with referred pain. *Am. J. Physiol., 133:*316, 1941.

91. GELLHORN, ERNST, and THOMPSON, L.: Muscle pain, tendon reflexes and muscular coordination in man. *Proc. Soc. Exp. Biol. & Med.*, 56:209, 1944.

92. WOLFF, H. G., GOODELL, H., and HARDY, J. D.: New evidence on the nature of cutaneous hyperalgesia. *Federation Proc.*, 8:170, 1949.

93. ECKARDT, L. B., McLEAN, J. M., and GOODELL, H.: Experimental studies on headache: the genesis of pain from the eye. *Proc. A. Res. Nerv. & Ment. Dis.*, 23:209, 1943.

94. ROBERTSON, S. B., WOLFF, H. G., and GOODELL, H.: Studies on headache: The teeth as a source of headache and other pain. *Arch. Neurol. & Psychiat.*, 57:277, 1947.

95. SIMONS, D. J., DAY, E., GOODELL, H., and WOLFF, H. G.: Experimental studies on headache: Muscles of the scalp and neck as sources of pain. *Proc. A. Res. & Ment. Dis.*, 23:228, 1943.

96. HARDY, J. D., GOODELL, H., and WOLFF, H. G.: Evidence on the nature of cutaneous hyperalgesia. *J. Clin. Investigation*, 29:115, 1950.

97. HEAD, HENRY, and HOLMES, GORDON: Sensory disturbances from cerebral lesions. *Brain*, 34:102, 1911.

98. KENDALL, D.: Some observations on central pain. *Brain*, 62:253, 1939.

99. MAGOUN, H. W.: An ascending reticular activating system in the brain stem. *Arch. Neurol. & Psychiat.*, 67:145, 1952.

100. FORSTER, O.: Symptomatologie der erkrankungen des Ruckemarks und seiner Wurzeln. *Bumke-Forsters' Handbuch der Neurol.*, 5:1, 1936.

101. BICKFORD, REGINALD G.: Experiments relating to the itch sensation. Its peripheral mechanism and central pathways. *Clin. Sc.*, 3:377, 1937-38.

102. BISHOP, GEORGE H.: Neural mechanisms of cutaneous sense. *Physiol. Rev.*, 26:77, 1946.

103. GRAHAM, D. T., WOLFF, H. G., and GOODELL, H.: Neural mechanisms involved in itch, "itchy skin," and tickle sensations. *J. Clin. Investigation, 30:*37, 1951.

104. ROTHMAN, STEPHEN: The nature of itching. *Proc. A. Res. Nerv. & Ment. Dis., 23:*110, 1943.

105. ZOTTERMAN, Y.: Touch, pain and tickling: an electrophysiological investigation on cutaneous sensory nerves. *J. Physiol., 95:*1, 1939.

106. BANZET, P. M.: *La cordotomie. Etude anatomique technique, clinique and physiologique.* Paris, Libraire Louis Arnette, 1927.

107. BISHOP, GEORGE H.: Responses to electrical stimulation of single sensory units of skin. *J. Neurophysiol., 6:*361, 1943.

108. LEHMANN, J. E.: The effect of asphyxia on mammalian A nerve fibers. *Am. J. Physiol., 119:*111, 1937.

109. LIVINGSTON, WILLIAM K.: *Pain Mechanisms.* A physiologic interpretation of causalgia and its related states. New York, MacMillan, 1943.

110. KARL, R. C., PEABODY, G. E., WOLFF, H. G.: The mechanism of pain in trigeminal neuralgia. *Science, 102:*12, 1945.

111. LENNANDER, K. G.: Ueber lokale Anesthesie und uber Sensibilitat in Organ und Gewebe, weitere Beobachtungen II. Mitt. a. d. Grenzgeb. d. Med. u. Chir., *15:* 465, 1906.

112. BLANKENHORN, MARION A., and FERRIS, EUGENE B., JR.: On the nature of aviators' bends. *Tr. A. Am. Physicians, 58:*86, 1944.

113. ROSENBLUM, D. E.: Nature and origin of altitude pains. *Am. Rev. Soviet Med., 1:*303, 1944.

114. HARPUDER, KARL, and STEIN, I. D.: Studies on the nature of pain arising from an ischemic limb. II. Biochemical studies. *Am. Heart J., 25:*438, April, 1943.

115. LEWIS, THOMAS: Pain in muscular ischaemia: its relation to anginal pain. *Arch. Int. Med., 49:*713, 1932.

116. CAPPS, JOSEPH A.: Pain from the pleura and pericardium. *Proc. A. Res. Nerv. & Ment. Dis., 23:*263, 1943.

117. WOLFF, HAROLD G.: *Headache and Other Head Pain.* New York and London, Oxford, 1947.

118. WOLFF, HAROLD G.: Headache mechanisms — a summary. *Proc. A. Res. Nerv. & Ment. Dis.,* 23:173, 1943.

119. WOLFF, HAROLD G.: *Headache—Mechanisms and Differential Diagnosis,* p. 1460 in Analysis and Interpretations and Symptoms, Experimental, edited by Cyril M. MacBryde, Philadelphia, Lippincott, 1944.

120. HUNTER, C. R., and MAYFIELD, F. H.: Role of the upper cervical roots in the production of pain in the head. *Am. J. Surg.,* 78:743, 1949.

121. KUNKLE, E. C., RAY, B. S., and WOLFF, H. G.: Experimental studies on headache: an analysis of the headache associated with changes in intracranial pressure. *Arch. Neurol. & Psychiat.,* 49:323, 1943.

122. KUNKLE, E. C., RAY, B. S., and WOLFF, H. G.: Experimental studies on headache: the mechanisms and significance of the headache associated with brain tumor. *Bull. New York Acad. Med.,* 18:400, 1942.

123. SCHUMACHER, GEORGE A., and WOLFF, HAROLD G.: Experimental studies on headache: A. Contrast of histamine headache with the headache of migraine and that associated with hypertension. B. Contrast of vascular mechanisms in pre-headache and in headache phenomena of migraine. *Arch. Neurol. & Psychiat.,* 45:199, 1941.

124. SUTHERLAND, A. M., and WOLFF, H. G.: Experimental studies on headache: Further analysis of the mechanism of headache in migraine, hypertension and fever. *Arch. Neurol. & Psychiat.,* 44:929, 1940.

125. FISHBERG, ARTHUR M.: Hypertension and Nephritis. Philadelphia, Lea, 1930.

126. ROBERTSON, H. S., and WOLFF, H. G.: Studies on headache: distention of rectum sigmoid colon and bladder as a source of headache in intact human subjects. *J. Arch. Neurol. & Psychiat.,* 63:52, 1950.

127. SCHUMACHER, G. A., and GUTHRIE, T. C.: Mechanisms of headache induced by distention of bladder and rectum in patients with spinal cord injuries. *Tr. Am. Neurol. A.*, 74:205, 1949.

128. WOLFF, H. G., KUNKLE, E. C., LUND, D. W., and MAHER, P. J.: Studies on headache: Induced mechanical stresses in the analysis of headache mechanisms. *Tr. Am. Neurol. A.*, 72:93, 1947.

129. WOLFF, H. G., and TUNIS, M. M.: Analysis of cranial artery pressure pulse waves in patients with vascular headache of the migraine type. *Tr. A. Am. Physicians*, 65:240, 1952.

130. OSTFELD, A., and WOLFF, H. G.: Studies in headache: participation of ocular structures in the migraine syndrome. *Mod. Probl. Ophthal.*, 1:634, 1957.

131. INMAN, V. T., and SAUNDERS, J. B. DeC.M.: Referred pain from skeletal structures. *J. Nerv. & Ment. Dis.*, 99:660, 1944.

132. TRAVELL, JANET, and BIGELOW, NOLTON: Referred somatic pain does not follow a simple "segmental" pattern. *Federation Proc.*, 5:106, 1946.

133. JONES, C. M.: Pain from the digestive tract. *Proc. Res. Nerv. & Ment. Dis.*, 23:274, 1943.

134. MACHELLA, E. T., DWORKEN, H. J., and BIEL, F. J.: Observations in splenic flexure syndrome. *Ann. Int. Med.*, 36:543, 1952.

135. WOLF, STEWART: Sustained contraction of the diaphragm; the mechanism of a common type of dyspnea and precordial pain. *J. Clin. Investigation*, 26:1201, 1947.

136. PALMER, WALTER L.: The pain of peptic ulcer. *Proc. A. Res. Nerv. & Ment. Dis.*, 23:302, 1943.

137. RAY, BRONSON S., and NEILL, C. L.: Abdominal visceral sensation in man. *Ann. Surg.*, 126:709, 1947.

138. LERICHE, R., and STRICKER, P.: Recherches experimentals sur le nerf presacre. *Bull. Soc. nat. Chir.*, 53:819, 1927.

139. CLELAND, J. P. G.: Paravertebral anaesthesia in obstetrics: Experimental and clinical basis. *Surg., Gynec. & Obst.*, 57:51, 1933.

140. MEIGS, J. V.: Excision of the superior hypogastric plexus (presacral nerve) for primary dysmenorrhea. *Surg., Gynec. & Obst.*, 69:723, 1939.

141. EDWARDS, W. B., and HINGSON, ROBERT A.: Continuous caudal anaesthesia in obstetrics. *Am. J. Surg.*, 57:459, 1942.

142. WOLF, STEWART, GOODELL, HELEN, and WOLFF, H. G.: Unpublished data quoted from—Wolff, H. G., *Headache and other Head Pains*. New York, Oxford, 1946.

143. CUSHNY, ARTHUR R.: *Pharmacology and Therapeutics*. Philadelphia, Lea, 1940.

144. PAPPER, E. M., BRODIE, B. B., and ROVENSTEIN, E. W.: Postoperative Pain: Its use in comparative evaluation of analgesics. *Surgery*, 32:107, 1952.

145. DODSON, H. C., and BENNETT, H. A.: Relief of postoperative pain. *Am. Surgeon*, 20:405, 1954.

146. RAY, BRONSON S.: The management of intractable pain by posterior rhizotomy. *Proc. A. Res. Nerv. & Ment. Dis.*, 23:391, 1943.

147. RAY, BRONSON: *The surgical treatment of angina pectoris*. Nelson's System of Medicine, New York, Nelson, 1951.

148. BINGHAM, J. R., INGLEFINGER, F. V., and SMITHWICK, R. H.: Characteristics of visceral sensation in man, as observed in normal subjects and patients with unilateral sympathectomy. *J. Clin. Investigation*, 28:771, 1949.

149. RAY, BRONSON S., and CONSOLE, A. D.: The relief of pain in chronic (calcareous) pancreatitis by sympathectomy. *Surg., Gynec. & Obst.*, 89:1, 1949.

150. GRANT, FRANCIS C.: Surgical methods for relief of pain in the head and neck. *Proc. A. Res. Nerv. & Ment. Dis.*, 23:408, 1943.

151. FRENCH, J. D., VON AMERONGEN, F. K., and MAGOUN, H. W.: Activating system on brain stem of monkey. *Arch. Neurol. & Psychiat.*, *68*:577, 1952.

152. STARZL, T. E., and WHITLOCK, D. G.: Diffuse thalamic projection system on monkey. *J. Neurophysiol.*, *15*: 449, 1952.

153. KOSKOFF, Y. D., DENNIS, W., LAZOVICK, D., and WHEELER, E. T.: The psychological effects of frontal lobotomy performed for the alleviation of pain. *Proc. A. Res. Nerv. & Ment. Dis.*, *27*:723, 1948.

154. CHAPMAN, L. F., THETFORD, W. N., BERLIN, L., GUTHRIE, T. C., and WOLFF, H. G.: *Behavioral compensatory and defense reactions after loss of known amounts of cerebral hemisphere tissue.* To be published.

155. VAN WAGENEN: Personal communication to Dr. A. E. Walker.

156. WATTS, JAMES W.: Personal communication.

157. WALKER, A. EARL: Personal communication.

158. HARDY, J. D., RAY, B. S., GOODELL, H., and WOLFF, H. G.: Unpublished data.

159. SCARF, J.: Personal communication.

160. RUFFIN, J. M., BAYLIN, G. J., LEGERTON, C. W. and TEXTER, E. C.: Mechanism of pain in peptic ulcer. *Gastroenterology*, *23*:252, 1953.

INDEX

Abdominal viscera, pain in, 66
Acetanilid, analgesic effect of, 88
Acetylsalicylic acid, analgesic effect of, 88, 89
ACTH, use of in painful conditions, 87
Addiction to morphine, 90
Alcohol, ethyl, effect of on thresholds for:
hearing, 27
pain, 27
smell, 27
touch, 27
vibration, 27
Alcohol injection, 91
Alcohol, use in painful conditions, 97
Alimentary tract, afferent pathways from, 75
American Indians, pain threshold of, 20
Aminopyrine, analgesic effect of, 88
Amytal, use of in muscle pains, 87
Analgesics, 13, 25, 35, 36, 37, 88, 89, 90, 91, 97
Analgesics, effect of on pain threshold, 13
Analgesics, use in painful conditions, 88
Anatomy and physiology of pain, 3
Angina pectoris, 86
Anoxia, differential effect of, on pricking and burning pain threshold, 17
Antibiotic agents, use of in painful conditions, 87

Antispasmodic agents, effects on pain mechanisms, 87
Apparatus, Elsberg, 26, 27
Apparatus for measuring pain threshold, 14
Argyll-Robertson pupil, 63
Armstrong, Dr. D., 19
Aristotle, 22
Arterial hypertension, headache associated with, 47, 58
Arteries, significance of pain and cerebral, in migraine, 57
Arteries, turgor in, in relation to pain, 59
Artery, common carotid, relation of pulsations to pain of migraine, 58
Artery, meningeal, relation of, to headache mechanisms, 57
Artery, temporal, relation of pulsations to pain, 58
Arthritis, rheumatoid, 87
Atropine, dosage and administration, 86
Attitude, influence of, on pain threshold, 13
Autonomic effects secondary to distension of rectum and bladder, 60
Autosuggestion, influence of, on pain threshold, 13

Backache, origin of, 47
Bacteraemia, headache with, 56
Banthine, 86
Beecher, H. K., 4
Bigelow, N. H., 12
Bishop, G. H., 43

[113]

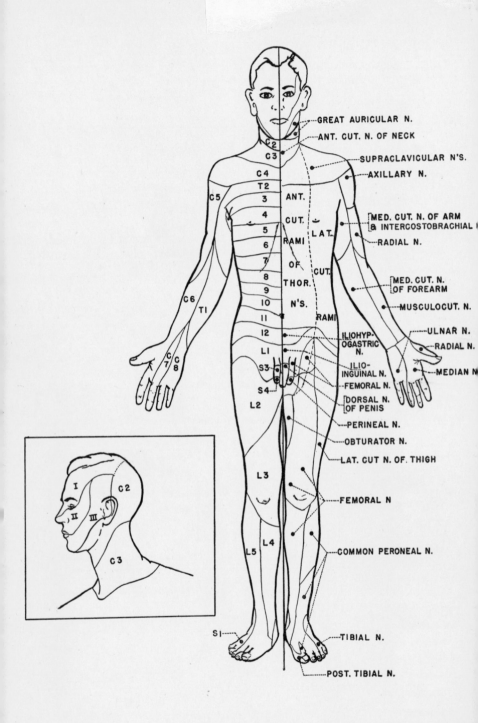

GREAT AURICULAR N.

ANT. CUT. N. OF NECK

C2

C3

SUPRACLAVICULAR N'S.

C4

AXILLARY N.

T2

C5

3

ANT.

4

CUT.

MED. CUT. N. OF ARM
& INTERCOSTOBRACHIAL

5

RAMI

LAT.

RADIAL N.

6

OF

7

CUT.

8

THOR.

MED. CUT. N.
OF FOREARM

9

N'S.

MUSCULOCUT. N.

C6

10

T1

11

RAMI

ULNAR N.

12

RADIAL N.

ILIOHYP-
OGASTRIC
N.

L1

S3

ILIO-
INGUINAL N.

C C
7 8

FEMORAL N.

MEDIAN N

S4

DORSAL N.
OF PENIS

L2

PERINEAL N.

OBTURATOR N.

LAT. CUT N. OF. THIGH

L3

FEMORAL N

L4

COMMON PERONEAL N.

L5

S1

TIBIAL N.

POST. TIBIAL N.

I

C2

II III

C3